LANDSCAPE WITH TREES

LANDSCAPE WITH TREES

WITHDRAWN

MILES HADFIELD

COUNTRY LIFE LIMITED LONDON

First published in 1967 by
Country Life Limited
Tower House, Southampton Street, London WC2
Printed in Great Britain by
Billing & Sons Limited, Guildford and London

Contents

	PREFACE	9
1	BEGINNINGS	11
	After the Ice	11
	Our Native Trees	15
2	FROM THE CELTS TO MEDIEVALISM	59
	The Woodlands Attacked	59
	Medieval Introductions	72
3	TUDORS AND STUARTS	79
	Spoliation	79
	New Arrivals	84
4	THE LANDSCAPE DEVISED	93
5	THE EIGHTEENTH CENTURY	109
	Crisis	109
	Novelties	121
6	THE RISE OF THE PICTURESQUE	127
7	LANDSCAPES BEYOND ENGLAND	142
8	THE NINETEENTH CENTURY	155
	Misguided Effort	155
	The Victorian Conifers	158
	The Victorian Landscape	172
9	THE TWENTIETH CENTURY	175
	GLOSSARY	184
	BIBLIOGRAPHY	186
	INDEX	193

Illustrations

*Illustrations, with the exception of No 57,
are from the author's own photographs*

1	Ancient durmast oakwood	*following page* 16
2	Relics of old oakwoods	16
3	A typical Cistercian site	16
4	Quality durmast oak	16
5	The elbow-like 'crucks' of pedunculate oak	32
6	Pollarded parkland oak	32
7	Common birch	32
8	Solitary thorn	32
9	Roadside wych elm	32
10	Midland hedgerow elms	32
11	East Anglian hedgerow elm	32
12	The smooth trunk of beech	32
13	Scots pine growing with birch	48
14	Scots pine	48
15	Centuries-old churchyard yew	48
16	Aged ash	48
17	Ash	48
18	The moisture-loving alder	48
19	The tower-like white willow	48
20	The spreading crack willow	48
21	The quaking aspen	64
22	Remains of coppiced wood of small-leaved lime	64
23	Remains of a medieval chase	64
24	Salvator's tree	64
25	Walnut	72
26	Sycamore	72
27	Wintour's Leap, near Chepstow	72
28	A larch wood	72

7

29	Lime avenue	*following page*	72
30	Norway spruce		72
31	London plane		72
32	Lebanon cedars		72
33	Brown's informality at Compton Verney, Warwickshire		80
34	Formality at Studley Royal, Yorkshire		80
35	Harewood, Yorkshire		80
36	Lombardy poplar		80
37	Tatton Park, Cheshire		96
38	Rudding Park, Yorkshire		96
39	Audley End, Essex		96
40	Early nineteenth-century oakwoods		96
41	Douglas fir		96
42	Monterey pine		96
43	Giant redwood		96
44	Wellingtonia		96
45	Monkey-puzzle		112
46	Thuja		112
47	Victorian conifers		112
48	The lime avenue, Clumber Park		112
49	Victorian ornamental woodland		128
50	Victorian conifers and water		128
51	Victorian conifers		128
52	Westonbirt, Gloucestershire, Brewer's Spruce		128
53	Bodnant, Denbighshire		144
54	Hergest Croft, Herefordshire		144
55	Benmore, Argyll		144
56	Rowallane, Co. Down		144
57	Eastwoodhill, Gisborne, New Zealand		160
58	Ebbw Vale, Monmouthshire		160
59	Lake Vyrnwy, Montgomeryshire		160
60	The new landscape, England		160
61	The new landscape, Scotland		176
62	The new landscape, Wales		176
63	The new landscape, Northern Ireland		176

Preface

THE OBJECT of this book is simple. It is to give some account of the part trees have played in forming the scenery of the British Isles from the earliest times to the present day. Apart from the activities of the builder, trees still form the least transitory feature of a scene that now changes, it seems, at an ever-increasing pace.

The subject falls into two parts. First, the history of the natural woodland, stretching back into remote time, and its subsequent wholesale destruction, exploitation and partial restoration. This story is often a sad and deplorable one of the squandering of natural resources, acts of economic folly with at times material danger to the country. To this day, economic forces – short term so far as destruction is concerned, long term as they relate to planting – dominate this aspect of our forest and woodland scene. It cannot be too strongly emphasised that this is so, and so, in our tiny group of islands, at a time when world supplies of timber may be decreasing dangerously, it must remain.

Secondly – and this concerns but a small proportion of our woodland – there is the English landscape garden. This is deeply involved with our philosophy, literature and poetry,[1] and with our landscape painting. The so-called 'natural' gardening that evolved from it has spread throughout the world, often taking the form of woodland gardens and even on the smallest scale largely dependent on trees.

These are the two themes of the book. One is major and fundamentally material, yet with singular visual consequences, the other minor and solely visual – at times poetic and even philosophical in its nature.

The present book is, from its nature, a compilation and an attempt to put together in some order information from many sources. The bibliography

---

[1] Since the text of this book was completed, Edward Malins, in *English Landscaping and Literature, 1660–1840*, has dealt adequately (and charmingly) with these subtle matters, which I have discussed only in the briefest outline.

9

at the end is therefore a list of the many authors to whom I am so greatly beholden. I fear that to keep this narrative continuous I have had to introduce subjects which I have already discussed elsewhere; for this inevitable tediousness I apologise.

My first-hand knowledge of the forests, woods and arboreta in the British Isles would be much less than it is were it not for the very many visits I have made, under the auspices of the Royal Forestry Society of England, Wales and Northern Ireland and its local organisations, to estates whose owners have always been at such pains to be helpful. Its *Quarterly Journal*, too, has provided an invaluable source of the day-to-day matters concerning both forestry and arboriculture, as has the comparable publication of the Royal Scottish Forestry Society.

Among numerous correspondents, I must single out Miss A. M. Coats, Mrs M. U. Jones, the late Edward Cahen, the late R. C. B. Gardner, the late Hon. Maynard Greville, A. F. Mitchell and J. D. U. Ward. Nor should I omit my brother John and his wife, who over many years have added on birthday and Christmas occasions to my library of works on landscape gardening.

And I have to thank W. Douglas Cook of New Zealand for information about and the photograph of his remarkable garden at Eastwoodhill.

Finally, I must draw the reader's attention to the closing paragraphs of this book. Their import is still far from generally comprehended, and is of great consequence both to the nation and the continued viability of our landscape.

CHAPTER ONE

Beginnings

AFTER THE ICE

MOST OF THE BRITISH ISLES would, if man ceased his present activities, return to woodland. In the City of London, on the piles of rubble left by the German air attacks, wind-borne tree seeds such as those of the sallows and birch were soon established. Following the destruction of rabbits in multitudes by myxomatosis many grassy, open beauty spots became covered with impassable scrub whose most permanent constituent was hawthorn bushes, from seeds scattered by birds. A neglected garden on heathy land will soon be covered with a dense growth of birch trees – the tiny, narrowly-winged seeds, like those of the sallows, being carried by the wind. These are colonisers. As their shade and demands for food gradually weaken the herbs, so conditions will, on many kinds of land, become suitable for larger trees, such as the oak. The process of change is a slow one, but eventually each type of reasonably fertile ground will become covered by a more or less stable cover of forest, whose constituent trees will be dependent on soil and site.

The woodland that covered so much of the British Isles before man came and threw his skill into the balance of nature colonised the country after the obliteration of most former vegetation by the eras of ice.[1] It has been suggested that there were ice-free pockets in our mountains of the north and west, and perhaps in that area of Ireland and south-western England whose flora, including the strawberry tree, is now a virtually isolated outpost of the Lusitanian plants native of Spain and Portugal and further into the Mediterranean.

[1] The information that follows is taken from scientific works and therefore, in view of the progress, or rather changing views, in that discipline, is not necessarily reliable, and should be treated with reserve.

However, in about 18000 B.C., along with the arrival of paleolithic man, came the trees – trees of the kinds that we know now, not those strange objects such as we see in fossils. Our island was then part of the European continent, with a continental, sub-arctic climate.

As the cold retreated, the tufted seeds of *Dryas octopetala*, of willows and the wind-borne seeds of dwarf birch were blown northwards and were able to germinate. That this can now be shown was so is due to the remarkable indestructibility of pollen grains, which have an identifiable fixed form. In particular, the pollen of wind-fertilised trees is preserved in peats. From a given layer of peat it is possible by chemical means to separate the pollen, microscopically identify it within certain limits, and by counting the grains of each kind, estimate its relative numerical abundance.

Since post-glacial times, the species concerned are identical with those growing today; their ecology (that is, briefly, the conditions and surroundings in which they grow) remains unchanged. Dating the deposits can be done by various means, such as observing the presence of datable relics and artefacts of man.

The technique of this pollen analysis was developed by the Swedes, van Post and Lagerheim, in the second decade of this century. Studies made over Europe showed consistent results. So far as the British Isles are concerned, Dr H. Godwin has over the last thirty or so years developed and refined the subject at Cambridge University, training a body of students whose expertise has now spread to other centres.

The key to this migration of plants, a very slow process in which a thousand years would have shown but little change, was the land bridge with the continent of Europe – where the Dogger Bank now is. Naturally, those plants nearest to us were the first to cross this bridge. They did not arrive here until after conditions had become suitable, having first to work their way northward over the Continent from the unglaciated areas.

This sub-arctic climate lasted nine or ten thousand years. It was followed by a thousand or so years of the pre-boreal climate which fluctuated, at times markedly, but by the end of the period had become decidedly warmer. Now the birches were moving up, followed by the Scots pines, hazels and oaks. The elm (assumed to be the wych) and alder reached eastern England.

In 7000 B.C. began the mesolithic age. With it came the boreal climate, warm and dry – warmer and pleasanter than that of today. Around the pinewoods hazel scrub, ideally suited for the new type of weather, grew vigorously and spread to Ireland and the north of Scotland. Over much of Britain the birch was dominant; in eastern England pine had suppressed this and, spreading westwards and northwards, began to get the upper hand as it moved, though birch retained its hold in the more extreme situations. Oak and elm enjoyed the improved conditions and increased. Lime increasingly entered forests.

After 2,000 or so years the rainfall increased. Hazel disliked this and decreased. It suited alder, which spread. The elm, oak and lime were happy, and thrived.

The Atlantic climate, warm and wet with high summer temperatures, had developed by 4000 B.C. Somewhere around this date (and here authorities differ considerably) the land link to Europe at last sank below sea level. The North Sea and the Atlantic met; Britain was an island. The area of water between us and the Continent was too great even for wind-borne seeds to cross. The last tree to slip in and reach southern England was the beech.

At this stage, our plant life and its distribution was very similar to what it would be today, but for man's activities. Our woodlands were preponderantly deciduous, dominated by oak, with much elm and lime. Hazel, as now, was abundant as undergrowth. Far less common (again, as today) were others that had crept in – holly, yew, box, apple, rowan, whitebeam, juniper, hedgerow maple, aspen, black poplar, hawthorn and, very localised, the arbutus. The sweet and bird cherries are considered natives. Up to now, the inhabitants were primitive and could have had little effect on the vegetation.

What would have happened if the land bridge had remained? Of the trees that have arrived here since the break, few are able to hold their own with our natives. Probably the Spanish chestnut would have come; it will, in suitable conditions, maintain itself in the warmer parts. Possibly the common spruce, which grew here before the ice age, but never returned, might again survive here. The sycamore lived a long way off, in the central European mountains, but is now firmly established and probably still spreading. The European larch is another mountain tree that would probably never have got here, and although it is now one of our commonest conifers, it is almost always planted.

The next stage, the neolithic age, brings, with the coming of a more intelligent type of man, the first major influence other than climate on our vegetation, and particularly on our woodlands. The ultimate effect of him and his successors on our general plant life was to be devastating, and on

our aboriginal woodlands virtually to destroy them, and later to recon-
struct them in an entirely new manner.

If we accept that the neolithic civilisation, fundamentally because of its
introduction of grazing, opposed to natural, humanless development,
occurred in about 2000 B.C. we can estimate man's staggering effect on
vegetation, now that we are all but 4,000 years on, by reference to the
List of British Vascular Plants (1958) – that is, plants growing 'wild'. This
includes aliens, plants brought in both purposely and accidentally by man
and now firmly established. Of the 2,895 names listed, over a fifth (22 per
cent) are believed aliens.

During the first thousand years of this neolithic age the sub-boreal
climate became drier. Woodland that had been destroyed by the bogs
formed in the previous wet period dried out and became re-established.
Pine, yew, beech and hornbeam (which had been here in small numbers
since early times) appreciated these conditions and increased locally.

There appear to be differing views on early agriculture. Some say it was
restricted to the drier chalk and limestone uplands, and the dry, sandy
soils. This is shown by the neolithic remains on the Yorkshire Wolds,
Salisbury Plain, Cotswolds, South Downs, Mendips, Southern Pennines
and the low rainfall areas of Pembroke and Anglesey. At that time the most
fertile land was covered with an impenetrable forest reigned over by
mighty and almost indestructible oaks, among which might be encoun-
tered the aurochs, bear, elk, wolf, lynx and wild boar.[1] Later authorities
doubt this and cite modern examples of clearing of dense woodland, where
not too wet, by burning, adding that this would increase potash content
and fertility. It is probable that the drier climate increased grazing land at
the expense of moisture-liking trees.

By the end of the neolithic period the two domestic animals most destructive to woodland were here, the sheep and goat. The former will
destroy seedling trees as they graze. Today, natural growth of woodland
from self-sown seed is impossible where sheep are present: to keep mountain sheep out of a plantation, even with modern fencing, is an extremely
expensive undertaking. The goat left to its own devices has in many places
reduced fertile lands to deserts. It is not improbable that its damaging effects
on our woodland in early times have been underestimated.

---

[1] The aurochs is believed to have survived in north Scotland into historic time, the
brown bear (valued as food) in parts of Britain until after the Romans left, the elk was
still here with the Romans, the wolf until the fifteenth or sixteenth century and later in
Scotland, the lynx into historic times and the wild boar until the seventeenth century.

The Bronze Age, at about 1000 B.C., coincided with a much damper climate. There was an increase in peat bogs. Pine and birch forests in Ireland, Scotland and northern England were choked by them. Their remains are dug up today.

By the time of the arrival of Iron Age man some 500 years later the climate had improved, and with a few fluctuations it has remained much the same since. With the coming of these iron users, and their need for fuel, was instituted in south-eastern England what was later to become perhaps the most violently destructive element in our forest history until the coming of two World Wars. One natural destructive agent should also be mentioned: the sea, which in some areas has destroyed acres of former woodland.

We have now reached a stage when man might well have begun introducing trees. Iron Age man would know the same native trees (that is, those kinds that arrive or survived in our islands without man's help) we identify today. It will be profitable to discuss the principal genera individually, for they formed the woodland from which our present scenery originated, with the exception of Ireland, which, after the last glaciation, was never reached by the beech, the limes and the hedgerow maple. In that place, therefore, they are introduced trees.

OUR NATIVE TREES

The Oaks

The vegetation of the British Isles – indeed, our early history – was set in a matrix of oakwoods. And, we are assured, when Macaulay's traveller from New Zealand takes his stand on that broken arch of London Bridge, in the vast solitude around him there will be on the river banks huge oakwoods, descended, perhaps, from the trees that in 1937 were dug up – the piles on which the bridge was built in 1176. Much of this book concerns the history of our oakwoods, but here we will look more closely at the trees themselves.

That we have more than one kind of oak has long been known. Authorities on the royal forests in early medieval times have been unable to explain the difference between oaks named in those times as *quercus* and *robur* (or in English, roer[1]).

---

[1] *Rouvre*, it is interesting to note, is now an Italian name for the durmast oak.

Some writers suggested that these terms (which are apparently always connected with the sale or gift of timber) might be concerned with differentiating, for example, maiden from pollard trees. Cox, however, pointed out that the two terms were maintained even to differentiate firewood.

Moses Cook, a man with ideas far in advance of his time, wrote of the oak in 1676: 'I shall not trouble you with the several kinds there be; though the learned J. Evelyn, Esq; reduced them to four . . . but if they were distinguished by several names, as we do our pears, you might find as many varieties, only according to the shape and taste of the acorn. For, as we know by experience, that several of our pear-trees grow pyramid-like, as the Oakmanberry and the Bordon-musk-pears, etc. and some likewise grow much spreading as the Winter-Bouchristian, the black Pear of Worcester, etc. even so do some of your oaks. Therefore if you desire aspiring trees, take care to gather your acorns off from such trees, or rather gather them from under some such trees. . . .' However, in 1733, another observant planter, the Earl of Haddington, wrote, 'authors write of different kinds [of oak], but I know of only one, which I had all from England.'

Not until much later was the problem of our native oaks solved – at least theoretically. In 1791 T. Nichols published his *Observations on Oak Trees*. In it, we find: 'There are two different sorts of oak growing in the [New] Forest, one the true English . . . the other called by woodmen in the forest durmast oak.'[1]

We know exactly what Nichols was discussing, for there is the drawing of a spray of oak in the Rev. Thomas Martyn's *Flora Rustica* of 1792 bearing the legend that it was drawn from a branch 'received from Mr Nichols out of the New Forest where it is known as Durmast Oak'. There is no doubt that this was oak apparently first described under the name *Quercus sessiliflora* by the English botanist R. A. Salisbury in 1796. Under this appropriate name (for the flower, and hence the acorn, is almost stalkless) our durmast oak was long known. But I said 'apparently', as the German botanist O. Schwarz discovered that in the eighteenth century

---

[1] It is interesting to note that when the thirteenth-century German natural philosopher Albertus Magnus described the oak it was the durmast he had in mind; he wrote that the acorn cup was not connected to the twig by a stalk, but was immediately upon it. This species is much the commoner in Germany; it is the constituent of the famous oakwoods of Spessart. A German name for it is *traubeneiche*, the oak with acorns clustered like grapes, a most appropriate description when this tree is fruiting heavily, and one I have heard used spontaneously in England.

1. Ancient durmast oakwood on the mountains near Beddgelert, Caernarvonshire.

2. Relics of old oakwoods; Ledbury, Herefordshire.

3. A typical Cistercian site; Rievaulx, Yorkshire.

4. Quality durmast oak grown under modern forestry conditions; Whitbourne, Herefordshire.

H. G. von Mattuschka had, in a study of the flora of Silesia, described the same oak as *petraea*, which means 'growing in stony places' – an equally good description, for the durmast does grow satisfactorily in mountains where the English oak will not thrive. Under the botanist's rules of nomenclature, the durmast or sessile oak is therefore *Quercus petraea*.

Our more familiar oak, the tree with the acorn cup on a stalk, or, in Linnaeus's phrase, the tree with acorns *cum longo pedunculo*, or pedunculate oak, goes by the name given to it by that botanist, *Quercus robur*, *robur* in Latin meaning oak-timber or oak-tree.

We can now come to a present-day, tidy description of our two oaks.

The pedunculate oak (*Q. robur*) has the acorns on long stalks and the leaves on very short stalks, the bases of the blades of the leaves having ear-like projections that curl round the stalk. The leaves are fairly regularly lobed, and examination of the underside with a lens often, but not invariably, shows the presence of single hairs (those on the acorn tip and acorn cup are, however, branched). It is described as the characteristic dominant tree of the heavy, and especially limy, soils such as clays and loams.

The durmast oak (*Q. petraea*) has acorns on short stalks and leaves on long stalks. The undersides of the leaves are greyish, due to the presence of hairs, sometimes minute, which are branched (stellate). The leaves vary greatly in size and form. Their base on some trees is narrowly wedge-shaped, on others with broad ears, but never tightly curled about the stalk. The lobes may be sharply pointed or rounded, or a combination of the two. These variations may be found on trees side by side in sites where the species appears to be anciently established and remote from the pedunculate oak, so that it seems unlikely that such trees are hybrids of a purer durmast oak with that species. This species is supposedly most at home on acid, sandy soils in the wetter parts of the British Isles (Plate 1). This is in part true, for it predominates on the actual mountains and hills of Wales and the north-west. But, equally, it is the predominant tree in many parts of the country on heavy soils with an alkaline reaction. In fact, there are few districts of the British Isles where it is not present.

As examples of its adaptability, we learn from Sir Cyril Fox that in the rich and fertile soil of Herefordshire the oak forest (which relics indicate was durmast) was so dense that in places Offa had no need to build his dyke (Plate 2).[1] After the heavy felling during the Napoleonic wars, the regrowth of oak trees in this same county was so dense as to produce

[1] The subsequent finding of earlier settlements within this area makes this conclusion doubtful.

spindly trees. At the other extreme, in Breckland, with the driest climate in England, and extremely harsh conditions, the durmast will seed itself on the poorest of soils and grow up through the heather.

How, then, has the name 'English oak' become attached, far beyond our country, to the pedunculate oak, Q. *robur*? Our claim that the British character resembles the oak is comparatively recent. Possibly that mildest of men, William Shenstone, was first to make it:

'All trees have a character analogous to that of men. Oaks are in all respects the perfect image of the manly character: in former times I should have said, and in present times I think I am authorised to say, the British one. As a brave man is not suddenly either elated by prosperity, or depressed by adversity, so the oak displays not its verdure on the sun's approach; nor drops it, on his first departure. Add to this its majestic appearance, the rough grandeur of its bark, and the wide protection of its branches. A large, branching, aged oak, is perhaps the most venerable of all inanimate objects.'

A little later, in 1759, David Garrick wrote the famous refrain to a song in his *Harlequin's Invasion*:

> *Heart of oak are our ships,*
> *Heart of oak are our men,*
> *We always are ready:*
> *Steady, boys, steady!*
> *We'll fight and we'll conquer again and again.*

We can only assume that our claim to this oak, which has a wide distribution in Europe, North Africa and West Asia, is due to our age-long insistence that our home-built ships were the best in the world only if they were made from our native oak.

It was therefore a surprise when, in 1950, Mark Anderson, a man both learned and practised in all that concerns British woods and trees, published his opinion that the English pedunculate oak was 'first introduced many centuries ago as a cultivated species in the south of England. Has spread from there, and by fresh introduction from the continent, all over the country.'[1]

This is a remarkable statement when one considers that if it is correct,

---

[1] What follows are my own views on the reasoning that prompted Anderson (a considerable historical scholar) to come to this conclusion. Unfortunately, his own full study of the subject remains unpublished.

our truly native oak was not identified until late in the eighteenth century, although it was then abundant in many parts of our island.

That there were very sound economic reasons for preferring the pedunculate to the durmast there can be no doubt, just as there are today equally valid reasons for preferring the durmast.

First, anyone who knows those districts where both kinds abound will after a few years observe that the pedunculate oak fruits much more heavily and much more regularly than the durmast; some authorities state that it will bear fruit at ten years old, much earlier than the durmast which is said not to do so until forty. For many centuries the acorns played a more important part in our economy than the timber, of which there was a superfluity and which was the enemy of pastoral man. In the royal hunting forests, they were food for the game. For the farmer, particularly the pig-keeper, they were valuable stock feed.[1] As we shall see in the Domesday survey, woods were often valued not by area or timber production, but by the number of swine they would maintain.

It is also said that the acorns of the durmast contained more tannic acid and were less palatable to pigs. My own modest researches into this dietetic point, however, showed that pigs are unaware of it.

Thus the heavier production of acorns is one most important reason for man to give it preference over the durmast from very early times. Even if in those days he did not propagate it, when clearing ground he would presumably save those trees he knew provided most food for his stock.

And this high production of acorns would, if it were an introduced tree, result in a natural increase in rate of production compared with the durmast.

The acorn is a heavy fruit that the elements of wind and water, so important as distributors of many tree seeds, do not carry about. A bounce of a yard or two after a fall is the most that can be expected. Even so, it does not stand much chance of germinating in the dry conditions and shade under its parent. Many learned papers have been written explaining the small number of seedlings in oak woods. But surely the explanation is obvious. A natural oakwood retains roughly the same density over the ages. An oak tree may be healthy and fill its allotted space for, perhaps, three hundred years. Therefore in that time it has only to add one successful tree to the wood to maintain the *status quo*. More seedling oaks are

[1] Over the centuries, however, years of glut have caused the deaths of cattle and horses, as they did so recently as during the autumn of 1964. A warning of this danger was given by Tusser in Elizabeth I's reign, 'For fear of a mischief, keep acorns for swine'.

usually found on the margins of oakwoods than within, and it is on the food value of the acorns that the oak relies for spreading its range.

A number of mammals eat and carry the acorns about, dropping some, but they do not take them far afield. Probably those that bury them help by inadvertently planting a few, those that they do not retrieve. (The most active planters, it is said, are pigs, which trample acorns into the ground and also help to conserve the young growth by eating slugs.)

Birds, however, are the major distributors. As young oak trees appear far away from any possible parent, it must be assumed that birds carry them there. Those that feed on acorns include pheasants, rooks, jackdaws, wood-pigeons and starlings. But the greatest consumer of acorns is the jay, which gathers them in large quantities in early autumn, using the long stalk of the pedunculate oak for picking and carrying the fruit. It then hides the acorns, usually in the ground, finding and eating some of them afterwards, at least into the spring, but losing many. The acorns are carried considerable distances. (The jay recovers this debt by building its nest in the oak and feeding its young on the caterpillars that infest the tree.)

The germinating power of the acorn, unlike hard seeds, such as those of the hawthorn, which pass unharmed through the bird's inside, is destroyed when eaten. Except when birds bury the fruit and do not return to collect their meal, distribution results because the large, awkward-shaped acorn is too much for the bird and is dropped. The existence of Wistman's Wood on Dartmoor, a wind-swept group of dwarf pedunculate oaks growing where, in theory, the durmast should grow, has for long been a problem. Anderson explains this incongruity by suggesting the acorns were carried by ravens, rooks and crows from Buckland and Tavistock Abbeys, both within ten miles of the wood, and where during the twelfth and thirteenth centuries the monks had (he claims) introduced the pedunculate oak. The wood stands on 'clatter', a mass of stone with interstices in which the oaks grow. The birds, he says, would collect the acorns and fly away with them until they came to this rough, stony patch up on Dartmoor. Here they would perch and rest. Every now and then an acorn would drop from a beak and roll into the soil under the clatter, where it germinated in the crack. It was there protected in its early stages from grazing animals and the searing wind, but when it reached the open, these two enemies kept it dwarf.

But did the Anglo-Norman monastic system require oaks that produce an abundance of acorns? The only order that concerned itself with agriculture was that of the Cistercians, or white monks. They first arrived at

Waverley in Surrey during the reign of Henry I. Not until their settlement at Rievaulx in Yorkshire during 1132 did they become powerful. Twenty years later they had some forty houses.

Unlike the other orders, these white monks were never based on quasi-urban buildings. We all know the typical Cistercian situation (Plate 3): the buildings beside a little river in a still, sequestered and romantic valley, whose steep sides are often covered with woodland. It is said that for financial reasons they settled in such places, because they were on non-manorial land. The material prosperity of the order lay in its success in clearing waste-land and woodland and bringing under cultivation large tracts of country to become the first, and for long the only, large-scale farmer in our islands. Their operations lasted some two hundred years. By the fifteenth century circumstances forced a change in policy, and their lands were rented to small farmers.

During that long period a great area of woodland on fertile sites must have been entirely cleared for corn, while the effect of sheep in preventing regrowth of woodland within range of their grazing must have been enormous: for example, in about 1250 it is estimated that Melrose Abbey had about 12,000 breeding sheep.

The extensive way these Cistercians covered the country is indicated if we name more of their abbeys, all in wooded districts. In Yorkshire alone they had Byland, Fountains, Jervaulx and Rievaulx. In the midland area were Croxden, Merevale, Rufford, Stoneleigh and Woburn. To the west and in Wales were Combermere, Dore, Valle Crucis, Strata Florida and Margam, and in the south there were Buckland and Cleeve.

Nowhere, so far as I can trace, is there any evidence that they planted trees other than apples and other fruit trees, osiers for basket making, and possibly walnuts for the oil that was expressed from the nuts. On the contrary, there is a great deal to show that their economy was entirely based on corn and sheep, both destructive of trees. Nor, situated in the heart of woodland (at the dissolution of the monasteries to become one of their most valuable and easily negotiated assets), was there any need to plant timber trees, though there is plenty of evidence that they cared for such woodland that they did not destroy.

There is much evidence that the pedunculate oak prevailed all over the country in medieval times. It is, perhaps, evidence of a kind that scientific workers, studying within their narrow disciplines, would be unaware of, for it is the work of artists, and particularly – as their work is the more durable – of sculptors.

No artist, I think, in a land of sessile oaks would invent the long-stalked acorn, nor would they provide their leaves with short stalks. From quite early in the middle ages sculptors used oak leaves and acorns as one of the principal decorative motives in our religious buildings, which were situated for the most part in those valleys and plains where the pedunculate oak supposedly predominates. And so it does in their sculptures. This can be seen particularly in that great collection of informal anecdotes of our history, the roof bosses. C. J. P. Cave tells us in the introduction to his collection of telephotos of these (in which we can leisurely examine their detail without straining our necks and using binoculars) that the oak was much favoured by church decorators. This is particularly so in what authorities call foliate masks, which in reality are the heads of the green-men, May-kings, May-men, Woose-men, or Jack-in-the-greens; the woodmen of our ancient pagan mythology, strange persons, often with faces like primitive Indians, gripping sprays of oak-leaves between their teeth. These secret pagan creatures once inhabited our woods to such effect that medieval carvers placed them, just to be on the safe side, in churches, generally discreetly high up in the roof where officiating clergy had no business to gaze. They are found also at the other and most unelevated extreme, under the seats or misericords.

These ancient wood-spirits, and scenes of woodland life, such as pigs feeding on mast under oak, can be seen in the cathedrals of Chester, Exeter, Hereford, Lincoln, Tewkesbury, Worcester and many other religious buildings, down to a church as tiny and remote as that of Gwernesney in Monmouthshire. Many of the representations are formalised, but there is no doubt about the design almost always being based on the pedunculate oak.

The most precise representations of foliage were carved during the period 1280 to 1310 – the period of realism. The limestone leaves of South-well cover the passage to, and vestibule of, the astonishing bower-like chapter room. Much has been written about the accurate carving of the leaves, but this has surely been exaggerated. Clearly cut though the foliage is, when one finds that Sir Albert Seward and Sir Edward Salisbury, distinguished botanists both, disagree in naming some of the species dis-played, one feels that natural liveliness rather than invariable botanical accuracy is the feature of this superb ornamentation. Nevertheless, we have a range of oak from true pedunculate to durmast, the pedunculate heavily predominating. Seward considered the sculptors had come across a hybrid in seeking their patterns. Certainly, today one finds both the pedunculate and durmast growing in the Dukeries not far away.

It seems, then, that to the medieval craftsmen the oak was what we still call the English or pedunculate oak, not the durmast. We must, it is true, accept that the superior craftsmen at least were travellers over Europe and worked to patterns. But no one can believe that the misericords in, for instance, Lincoln were other than by Englishmen working from what they had seen.

The monasteries disappeared, and as they did so another and eventually vastly more important advantage than the acorns of the pedunculate oak came to the front.

If we examine a vigorous winter shoot of the durmast we shall find that the main growth bud is on the same axis as the shoot. The next year's main longitudinal growth will continue along the same axis.

In the pedunculate, on the other hand, the growth bud is normally at an angle to the main shoot.

The result is that the durmast when grown in good conditions is a straight-trunked and lofty tree (Plate 4), while the pedunculate is round-headed, with a multitude of zig-zag twigs, the heavier branches formed like giant elbows.

Now we are dealing with the timber, not acorns. Pedunculate, by modern scientific standards, is indistinguishable from durmast. Both, therefore, equally provide one of the most useful timbers in the world. It is tough, strong, very durable, and our finest structural timber. There is, however, one singular difference. The durmast timber is comparatively straight. The pedunculate is full of curves, angles and a rich variety of shapes, ideally suited for the 'crucks' of houses, the hulls of ships[1] and a multitude of structural jobs which, during the nineteenth century, were rapidly replaced by iron and steel (Plate 5).

From the time of Elizabeth I onwards we shall see that again and again our island economy suffered from a shortage of not only pedunculate oak, but of the right quality of it, which might be attributed to climate, soil or genetic strain.

To ensure these elbowed trees, oaks were always grown widely spaced. Evelyn (1664) wrote 'of the need in His Majesty's forests of large spreading oaks . . . especially recommended for the excellency of the timber . . . they require room and space to amplifie and expand themselves, and would therefore be planted at more remote distances, and free from all incumbrances.'

[1] As will be seen later, we had little or no native timber suitable for masts; this was, from early times, mostly imported.

At the end of the next century we have Gilpin, who makes an accurate analysis of this growth form of the pedunculate oak, writing, 'it is not the erect, stately tree, that is always the most useful in ship building; but more often the crooked one, forming short turns and elbows, which the shipwrights and carpenters commonly call the knee-timber'; and Marshall, 'open woods are adapted . . . for the purpose of raising timber for ship-building when crookedness is required . . . It follows that no timber tree whatever, but the oak, can be raised with propriety in open woods, and this only when a supply of ship timber is intended.'

This uneconomic open spacing led to the growth beneath the oaks of sweet chestnuts, which are cut back to produce poles before they can interfere with the oaks – a matter discussed under that species.

Thus, first came the demand for a heavy yield of acorns, to be followed shortly by the need for the right type of structural timber, from Norman times, or perhaps earlier, until the nineteenth century. These caused Englishmen to discriminate against the durmast and prefer the pedunculate oak. As early medieval illustrations from all over Britain (particularly those of an unsophisticated kind) almost invariably show the distinctive long-stalked acorn, it seems quite impossible to accept that the tree bearing them was introduced, and had become almost universal by medieval times. (It is impossible to separate the pollen grains of the two species.)

One may suggest that not only were our oakwoods devastated from the day when man needed their fertile soils for food, but that the distribution of the two species was subsequently changed by him, thus causing the comparative rarity of durmast, except in places where it was more likely to be overlooked.[1] The reason for this must surely be that as the oakwoods were cleared, when any opportunity arose for the return, in even limited numbers, of the tree, it would be the pedunculate that would come in first. This was because of its earlier and more prolific fruiting and greater ease with which the acorns could be transported.

We know, too, that as early as the beginning of the eighteenth century man was to some extent discriminating against durmast, for Nichols reported on the 'bad consequences of not attending to this choice' of acorns for propagation (i.e. pedunculate rather than durmast).

We know, too, that in the early nineteenth century both New and

[1] For example, a survey made in 1861 of Herefordshire's greatest oak trees revealed that thirty-one were pedunculate and thirty-three significantly 'the rare (sic) sessile species'.

Dean Forests were purposively planted predominantly with pedunculate oak, though ecologists tell us that large areas of both would naturally be a habitat of durmast.

So, one may conclude that through man, helped particularly by birds,[1] great areas of natural durmast have been replaced by pedunculate, though that species could not survive on, for example, the rocky hills in the west although it has often made its way on to the lower, more fertile ground there.

So much has been written about the need for tough, strong and crooked timber for ships that the importance of the oak in building has been overlooked.

The curved 'crucks' of early houses differentiated the houses of those countries having oakwoods from those where the straight pole-like conifers predominate. The curve, its concavity inwards, gave extra head room.

On a vaster scale are the curved arch braces in many churches and buildings, such as Westminster Hall. There are also the huge straight beams, probably of durmast, made from oaks such as we no longer possess. Recall, for example, the great piece of oak on which hangs the roof of the chapter house in York Minster, or the vast beams of a tithe barn such as Bredon.[2]

It may be mentioned that wood other than oak is found in wooden-framed buildings. The house agent's 'wealth of old oak' in interiors may be, particularly in East Anglia, elm. Sweet chestnut, which, it is sometimes claimed, has been used in the framing of churches in particular, is extremely rare.

Brown oak is timber that is of a rich brown colour, variously marked. Though strong, it is used for ornamental purposes. The colour is due to the presence of a fungus, whose activity is stopped by seasoning.

Then there was that important by-product, oak bark for tanning leather. In 1787 the Hon. John Byng noted during his travels that at Chepstow 'on the quay were immense piles of bark for exportation to Ireland'. This was from Dean, and though a little oak bark is still used, other materials began to replace it in the early part of this century. There is some evidence that the bark with the most tannic acid came from durmast: I have been told by one who recollects an old firm of tanners

---

[1] M. L. Anderson in 1952 acutely remarked on the failure of ecologists to notice what he called 'avificial' woods.

[2] The tallest known oak in Britain today, at Whitfield, Herefordshire, is 135 feet high.

that the best bark came from a district where that species is universal.

The bark is stripped in April and May. Though for centuries there has been argument over the right season for felling oaks to gain the best timber, in fact the extra value of the bark made late spring felling almost universal.

Tan bark had other uses. When freshly removed from the tanner's vats, it was put into hot-beds. The moderate heat from its fermentation lasted much longer and at a more even temperature than that of the classic hot-bed made from dung. It would seem that this system was introduced from Holland about 1720, and made possible the cultivation of plants and the germination of seeds that had formerly proved difficult or impossible. By this means Philip Miller, gardener at Chelsea Physic Garden from 1722 to 1770, is known to have raised and cultivated many new and rare plants with success. The spent tan, well into the present century, was spread on the roads outside the houses of the dangerously ill to reduce the noise of the clattering horse-drawn vehicles.

Another feature of oak timber is its great durability when buried under the ground. It was used for coffins in the Bronze Age round barrows; it is still used by the *élite* who are prepared to pay the extra cost over the other coffin timber, elm. Medieval wells have been found lined with hollowed oak trunks. Stephen Switzer, garden designer and expert on hydraulics, wrote in 1729: 'The very best kind of wooden pipe is oak, which indeed is very strong and lasts a great while, there being some trees of that kind which (under my supervisal) were dug out of the foundations of Blenheim Bridge that were tho' as black as ebony yet as sound as Brazil[1] and might in all probability have no other date than the Deluge itself.'

Oaks were used as boundary marks and, as will be mentioned later, in Anglo-Saxon times particularly these gave their names to many settlements. Of most ancient origin is the element *derw*, found, for example, in such names as Derwent. In Ireland the comparable 'derry' is today present in some 1600 place-names out of a total of 62,000 – a memorial to the destruction of oakwoods in that now comparatively treeless country.

What of the age of oaks, for which high figures are so often claimed? It is extremely difficult to calculate the age of an obvious veteran and reliable records are scarce. There is the stump of the Newland oak in the Forest of Dean, which it is not unreasonable to assume goes back to the

---

[1] Presumably Brazil wood, a tropical species of *Caesalpina*.

thirteenth century. Kett's oak at Ryston, Norfolk, was quite possibly a sizable tree in 1547.

As to size, in addition to the Whitfield oak already mentioned, among the biggest in the country recorded by A. F. Mitchell (excluding pollards[1]) are pedunculates at Marchmont, Berwick (128 feet high × 14 feet 10 inches), and Sparkford, Somerset (70 feet × 32 feet 3 inches).

Of durmasts, he records a tree at Nettlecombe, Somerset (120 feet × 21 feet 1 inch), and Shobdon, Herefordshire (90 feet × 29 feet 1 inch).

Ecologists have divided our woodlands rather approximately into fifteen natural communities. Some of these are only transitional. Many have been, and are continually being, interfered with by man, particularly when he began to let sheep graze comparatively unrestrictedly over wide areas.

Of these communities, four include the oak, and must represent in their total by far our biggest area of apparently 'natural' woodland which might well continue to exist if man, and the animals associated with him, ceased to exist.

The major one is called the moist oakwood association; this probably originally covered much of the British Isles. It is found on the heavier soils, particularly in the areas of lighter rainfall. In the west, it is typically that type of oakwood with many ferns, the greater wood rush and numerous mosses. Holly is often present.

The dry oakwood community is found on the more porous and sandy soils, and on the rocky hillsides, where it is often little more than scrub. Its typical plants include the creeping seft-grass (*Holcus mollis*), bracken and bluebells.

Next comes the oak–birch community. The presence of birch, a tree of light, heathy soils, indicates that this association is found on less fertile soils. In these woods there is a wider range of shrubs, particularly those associated with heathland, than in the others. When cleared, this type of forest tends not to grow again naturally and develops into pure heath.

Wherever the oak grows, it will not tolerate stagnant moisture. This, when changing geographical circumstances have brought about its existence, causes 'stag-headed' trees, which so aptly describes those sad ancients dying in the top. Excessive drainage which seriously lowers the water-table can have the same effect on well-established trees.

Though not the work of nature, the last 'community' is the scattered

---

[1] A pollard grows to a disproportionately wide diameter compared with a maiden – that is, a tree in a natural, unlopped stem.

planting of oaks – or perhaps the retention of oaks when land was cleared – that is such a feature of our parkland (Plate 6), as are our hedgerow and other occasional oaks no doubt often 'planted' by birds and beasts.

The Birches

In every way the birches are a contrast to the oak. Light and airy, in comparison short-lived, and at present economically of little value.

At the beginning of the seventeenth century William Browne, in his *Britannia's Pastorals*, referred aptly to 'the cold-place-loving birch'. In 1664 John Evelyn elaborated: 'it will thrive both in the dry and wet, sand and stony, marches and bogs; the water galls, and uliginous parts of forests that hardly bear any grass'. The birches do, indeed, reach more northerly latitudes and climb higher up the mountains than any other of our native trees, except the rowan. Surprisingly little attention has been given to them by botanists – possibly because until recently they had been regarded sylviculturally as a nuisance, with timber of negligible value and with whippy stems that thrash and damage more valuable species.

As might be expected, the birches were among the first trees to cross the land bridge from the Continent as the ice receded northwards. They are both colonisers and light-loving trees, so that when a more permanent species, such as oak, gains a footing, the shade cast eventually stifles them. Natural birch wood can, however, be so dense that it will inhibit bird and other wild life quite as effectively as a dense stand of conifers. Numerically, birches are probably the commonest trees in the British Isles, growing almost everywhere, though not liking chalk.

Apart from the dwarf birch, *Betula nana*, restricted to the extreme north of England and Scotland, we have two distinct species. Probably the commoner is that known to botanists as *B. verrucosa* (or *pendula*). The first name is appropriate, for verrucose, or warty, accurately describes the twigs, which are rough, with numerous pale-coloured warts. Except on young trees, the shoots are not downy. The leaves are drawn out in a very distinct sharp point at the apex. The second name *pendula* is sometimes a misnomer, for the most erect-growing variant of our birches belongs to this species. The base of old trees becomes blackened and fissured into rectangular bosses. This tree is the commoner on dry, sandy soils (Plate 7).

Our other species is *Betula pubescens*. Here again the botanical name is apposite. The twigs are downy and feel soft when one draws them through the fingers. The leaves are rounder, more regularly toothed and without the sharply drawn-out point. The old trunks do not fissure into rectangular bosses. This is more likely to be found in 'the water-galls and uliginous parts of forests'. Botanists originally, therefore, tidily described two easily separated species, which grow over a considerable area of Europe and in parts of Asia. That there are intermediates between the two was at first readily explained by hybrids arising between them, for they often grow close together. Comparatively recently it has been shown by geneticists that their respective chromosomes are so formed that hybrids cannot take place. Several sub-species and races are described, but in some regions, such as parts of Scotland, variations are so considerable that it seems quite impossible to make tidy arrangements. The true status of our birches remains a puzzle.

Birches seed prolifically. The male, pollen-bearing catkins, more or less pendulous and tightly rolled-up, are seen as soon as the leaves fall. The females are much smaller and stand upright on the twigs. In about the middle of April the male catkins lengthen and become flexible, liberating their pollen. At the same time, from the females, still insignificant and erect, the minute crimson stigmas emerge. The pollen is carried to them by the wind. Individual trees in a plantation vary greatly in the date that this happens (as well as of leafing) and three or even four weeks may separate the first and last trees. After fertilisation the female catkins lengthen and become pendulous; the males soon fall.

The catkins begin to break up in November, the last remaining seed usually being scattered by the January gales. As early as August, however, one may stand under a tree and be surprised by the seeds and fragments of the catkins drifting down – the litter under the trees is sometimes as thick as a natural seedfall. The cause is birds extracting the seeds, now presumably fat enough to have food value. I have watched blue tits and greenfinches stripping the catkins and no doubt other seed-eating birds also rip them up. A good deal of seed inevitably falls, and I have wondered if, like ash seed, it will germinate before it is apparently ripe.

The timber of the birch has always been considered almost valueless except in mixed woodland districts where small turneries have long been established. These factories, now fewer in number than formerly, but larger and considerably mechanised, still use large quantities of birch wood. In roughly thirteen foot lengths, it is first partially peeled by hand, then stacked to season for a year. It is then converted by automatic machinery into many small objects such as brush backs and handles. The wood takes modern, brightly-coloured, glossy paints extremely well.

It is used, too, for wood pulp. In the Scandinavian countries birch has long been used for plywood – but there, either because of climate or for genetic reasons, the trees are of better quality.

In recent years it has seemed to a band of pioneers that far greater use could be made of this tree, so abundant in the British Isles, yet economically regarded as a weed. They have studied the production of trees with straight grain suitable for plywood, turnery and pulp, and with irregular grain producing decorative timber, such as 'flamy' birch. As it is, modern forestry practice has shown conclusively that new plantations become more quickly established where a light cover of birch is left on the ground.

One use of birch, formerly important, has now quite disappeared. A branch was wounded and the sap caught in a can. 'The liquor', observed Evelyn, 'is esteemed to have all the virtues of spirit of salt, without the dangers of acrimony; most valuable for the dissolving of the stone in the bladder. Helmont shows how to make a beer of the water; but the wine is a most rich cordial . . . exquisitely made, it is so strong, that the common sort of stone bottles cannot preserve the spirits, so subtile they are and volatile and yet it is gentle, and very harmless in operation within the body, and exceedingly sharpens the appetite, being drunk *ante pastum*.' The sap itself, which flows profusely from pruning wounds in winter, is quite tasteless.

A former use of birch was in the iron workings of the Suffolk Weald. Examination of charcoal remains show it to have been the most frequently used tree, much more so than oak. Birch twigs, laid in the vats, played an essential part in the making of malt vinegar. Oil distilled from the bark was – perhaps still is – used for the finishing of Russian leather, giving it a distinctive odour. According to H. J. Elwes this oil is also the best prevention against midges.

Perhaps, therefore, our birch woods have a future that is not purely aesthetic. At all seasons they are beautiful, not least in early spring, when the swelling buds give them a plum-coloured bloom quite unlike that of any other tree.

The Hawthorn

Like the elms, the hawthorn or white thorn has been intimately connected with hedgerows and enclosures at least from Roman times, and probably much earlier. The spiny branches laid and interlaced form the barrier itself: the living or quickset fence.

Like the elm too, it is a light-loving tree and seldom found in woodlands, except on their margin or in open glades. It forms impenetrable scrub on certain types of waste land, but this eventually becomes broken up into individual units.

The hawthorn is, indeed, a coloniser. The later stages of a thorn wood were described by W. H. Hudson: 'The most perfect thorn wood is that where there is room for a person to walk freely about in it and see every tree . . . its beauty is greatly enhanced by the character of the open sunlit ground it grows on . . . turf closely eaten down by the innumerable rabbits.'

In the wilder, heathy places, the thorn is often found as a solitary, gnarled tree of great character (Plate 8). On wind-swept sea coasts, or exposed hills (it will grow at 1800 feet) the form is often fantastic.

In the middle of May,[1] or the first days of June, there is no lovelier sight in those parts of our islands where hedges grow freely, than the

> . . . fair blooming of the hawthorn tree
> *Who, finely clothed in robe of white,*
> *Feeds full the wanton eye with May's delight.*

When one considers how destructive man has been to the delights of his wanton eye, it is pleasant to be able to credit him with the planting of these thousands of miles of hedges, largely done in the early years of the nineteenth century.

In winter, the scarlet haws make a cheerful sight, particularly in those districts where mistletoe grows in the trees to form a strange combination of greenery, naked twigs and scarlet. In due course birds, notably fieldfares, redwings and blackbirds, strip the trees and distribute the hard nutlets, which are the seed, in their excrement.

The hawthorn is deeply involved in folklore, more so than any tree except the ash – whose traditions have died out, whereas those of the thorn are remembered still: de la Mare recalled them in one line:

> *The hawthorn hath a deathly smell.*

The cult of the hawthorn is directed to one purpose, the prevention of destruction or disfiguration of the tree. It is a localised cult. Only in certain parts of the British Isles does the cutting and bringing into the house of flowering sprays (with their deathly scent) presage death in the house. Only

[1] The application of the name 'may' to hawthorn is comparatively recent. The may of May Day celebrations consisted of all sorts of greenery; hawthorn is not normally in flower on 1st May, either by the present or old calendars.

in Ireland is a solitary hawthorn the trysting place for the 'little people' – and woe betide those who damage the place of their meeting. A Cromwellian who destroyed the Glastonbury thorn[1] was stabbed in the eye and henceforth was monocular.

The frequence of solitary thorns of distinguished shape in comparatively treeless landscapes has been mentioned, and was also noted by Milton:

> *Every shepherd tells his tale*
> *Under the hawthorn in the dale . . .*

The implication is that on the bare downland where the flocks live, the shepherd chooses as his headquarters, so to speak, an old thorn.

There are probably more place-names embodying 'thorn' in the sense of hawthorn (names embodying blackthorn can usually be separated), evolved from the Old English, even than from oak. It seemed to me that these thorn place-names would be outside the areas of dense woodland. Following this suggestion, P. W. F. Brown, working for the Folklore Society, made a sketch map of England, based on the Ordnance Survey, shading the approximate areas of forest land from Roman times to the accession of Alfred in 871. On this he superimposed place-names having 'thorn' as their element. With two exceptions they all stand in the open country, with a slight predominance in Yorkshire and Lancashire and a mere scattering in the counties bordering the English Channel.

It is not surprising, therefore, to find such enthusiasm towards preserving trees that were once landmarks in bare country.

The common whitethorn[2] is named *Crataegus monogyna*, the epithet referring to the presence of only one style in the flower and one seed in the haw. It has a wide distribution throughout Europe (except Iceland) and throughout the Mediterranean region eastward to Afghanistan. We have as a native another thorn, *C. oxyacanthoides*,[3] distinguished by the presence of two but sometimes one or three styles in the flower, with a corresponding number of seeds, and by the fact that it is a woodland tree, growing mostly in the eastern counties, where it is locally common. Elsewhere, it is usually absent. Generally it is on the decline in this country, partly and accidentally due to modern forestry methods, and partly because it hybridises freely

---

[1] This legend does not come within our view. This famous thorn is a variant of the common thorn that flowers precociously, comparable with the variant of the cherry *Prunus subhirtella* called 'Autumnalis' grown in our gardens.

[2] In some heavy soils the flowers have a distinctly pink tinge when they mature.

[3] Also known as *C. oxyacantha*, oxyacantha being the name of some spiny shrub mentioned in the writings of Theophrastus, who worked with Aristotle.

5. The elbow-like 'crucks' of pedunculate oak; Sutton Park, Warwickshire.

6. Pollarded parkland oak; Colwall, Herefordshire.

7. Common birch, Led-
bury, Herefordshire.

8. Solitary thorn; Sutton
Park, Warwickshire.

9. Roadside wych elm; Naseby, Northamptonshire.

10. Midland hedgerow elms.

11. East Anglian hedge-row elm; Ipswich, Suffolk.

12. The smooth trunk of beech; Pendugwm, Montgomeryshire.

with the common thorn, thus losing its identity, the hybrid producing fertile seeds.

C. oxyacanthoides, while scarcely having an individual effect on the landscape, is of consequence in roadside planting, parks and gardens, for from it spring the abundance of double white and pink, single scarlet and other coloured forms of hawthorn so often planted.

The Elms

The elms, all but one species, play a distinctive part in what might be called the fieldscape. For many thousands of miles their statuesque, erect and dignified forms parade, a little irregularly, along our hedgerows, often evidence of man's tree planting over many centuries around the settlements and open spaces from which he anciently cleared the natural forest and of the eighteenth and nineteenth century era of enclosure. None of the botanically rather complex species, hybrids or variants that he used for these purposes is a naturally woodland tree; all need air and light around them.

The exception is our native wych elm, *Ulmus glabra*,[1] a large tree with a domed crown whose branches spread widely and droop at their ends. Old specimens often have two or three trunks. This tree was an important immigrant prior to, and then constituent of, our deciduous woodland in the time of the Boreal climate. Today, it is found scattered all over the British Isles, more frequently in the north and west, where it often grows in rough hedges, by roadsides (particularly the Roman roads) and along streams (Plate 9). It also grows in ashwoods and oakwoods, particularly on limestone. In the west of England one finds areas of wych elm which are the relics of coppiced trees. What the use of the poles was is now unknown, but as in Roman times the elm was used for supporting vines, it may have been used here for such purposes as hop-poles.

Unlike the other elms found in this country, the wych elm reproduces itself freely from seed, which is winged and so distributed by the wind. It also hybridises – the so-called Dutch elm and the magnificent Huntingdon elm probably have it in their constitutions.

Although wych elm is normally a gnarled and crooked tree whose timber is ill-shaped, if grown close so that the boles are straight the wood is

---

[1] The name wych (from *wican*, bend) was in the past applied to other elms, and to several trees and shrubs with flexible branches. *Glabra*, botanically meaning smooth or bare, is an unfortunate epithet for a tree whose leaves are particularly rough and hairy. It relates (it is said) to the twigs; these too, are covered with down when young, but become smooth.

C

valued. As with our other elms (which are much straighter), it has the particular quality that if it is kept either in permanently wet or permanently dry situations, it is very long-lasting. For this reason it supplies the boards for the poor man's coffin and the interior studding for a good many houses allegedly displaying a 'wealth of old oak'. It is one of the timbers most frequently found in underwater piles and old wooden water pipes. It was much used by the wheelwright. The wych elm, on account of its flexibility, was, according to John Aubrey writing in the seventeenth century, used as the next best timber after yew by bowyers. A tree of this species blown down at Oxford in 1911 was probably then the largest timber tree in Britain, girthing 28 feet 3 inches and being 143 feet high. Large trees are not now uncommon.

The wych elm has a wide distribution, growing over most of Europe and north and west Asia. Scarcely affecting the landscape, other than those of cemeteries, and gardens, are its several weeping forms, which were apparently first collected and cultivated at the beginning of the nineteenth century.

The hedgerow elm, *Ulmus procera* or *campestris*[1] (Plate 10), the most notable tree in the landscape of the midlands, has, on the other hand, a most restricted natural area. It is limited to the British Isles except, apparently, for parts of Spain, where the trees (according to Evelyn) were imported by Philip II. It becomes less common the farther north one goes, and is absent from some of the eastern counties. Unlike the wych elm, it naturally takes a bolt-upright stature, with a massive, little-branched trunk – providing excellent material for pipes and boards.

Its origin brings us to two other points of interest when discussing the elms of the fertile plains – their use as fodder plants (the tree carries its leaves very late) and as boundary marks (its head casts little shadow). This involves other species and hybrids, such as the smooth-leaved elm (*U. carpinifolia*),[2] a tree found principally in east and south-east England, and the study of early settlements and agriculture – subjects equally of great botanical and historical interest which have been studied by R. H. Richens, of whose conclusions no more than some of the salient points can be mentioned here.

Richens first takes into account the fact that the elms he studies, unlike the wych elm, seldom, if ever, produce fertile seed. They increase only (again unlike the wych elm) by means of suckers. Each separate group or

---

[1] *Procera* means tall, and *campestris*, growing in fields.
[2] *Carpinifolius* means with leaves like hornbeam.

population – such as that in a hedgerow – must have been planted by a man and retained its individual character since that time. He found that in many instances populations not far from one another, but unable to unite by suckering, were botanically distinct.

He largely based his studies on trees along the old parish boundaries; these boundaries have usually remained unchanged since medieval times, and, as has already been mentioned, may contain descendants (vegetative and unchanged in the case of the elm) of the trees mentioned in Anglo-Saxon charters. He chose East Anglia, where it has long been known that different species and races of elms meet, disappear, or are intermingled (Plate 11).

Some of the conclusions Richens reached are surprising. He considers that the elms of East Anglia along these old boundaries have been there at least since the Roman occupation. (In Italy, the use of and knowledge of the different kinds of elms for forage, timber and as a support for vines was mentioned by several ancient authors.) He suggests that the smooth-leaved elm, *U. carpinifolia*, may go back even earlier, to introductions during the later Iron Age: its present distribution in East Anglia, north-east Midlands, and parts of Sussex, Hampshire and Glamorgan links up with settlements of that era.

Our hedgerow elm, *U. procera*, he believes to have originated, at some unknown date, perhaps as a single tree, in the Midlands: possibly the very late fall of its foliage might have drawn attention to it, and certainly the straightness and large diameter of the trunk, with long lengths between the branches, well suited for pipes, would single it out as a valuable tree. Gradually, it was propagated and taken into the surrounding districts. Yet today it has not reached Cambridge, Norfolk, Suffolk and parts of the adjoining counties; is this because those areas already had an adequacy of elm trees?

The subsequent history of our hedgerow elms is that of our hedges, and therefore of the long continuance of enclosure acts. These were particularly numerous during the eighteenth and early nineteenth centuries. Propagation was easy: rooted suckers were struck off with a chisel from an old tree. The suckers spread along the line of the hedgerow, but were grazed off in the fields.

The English elm was also a principal tree in the avenues of our seventeenth- and early eighteenth-century gardens. It had decided advantages over its rival, the European lime. It was easier to produce – lime had to be layered – held its leaves very much later and was just as erect. It did not have the fragrant flowers, yet an elm in the earliest days of spring covered with the myriad crimson stamens of the flowers on the leafless twigs is an encouraging and most lovely sight. (The green disc-like fruit forms about three weeks after flowering, and in some years gives an impression of precocious leafing.)

There are several other hybrids, species and microspecies of our elms observed by botanists, most of them not profoundly different from wych, English and East Anglian elms to the unskilled observer.

Two, however, are distinct. Just as one notices on passing into the eastern counties that the hedgerow elms have more sinuous trunks and finer, lace-like twiggery, so as one enters parts of south Devon and Cornwall one observes that the elms are almost universally of a gaunt, narrowly-erect and quite distinct form; if one goes in May, it will also be noticed that this elm is much later leafing than those in the colder midlands. The Cornish elm is usually known as *Ulmus stricta*.

The other erect, but much more spire-like, and usually larger and more graceful tree than the Cornish elm is the Wheatley or Jersey elm (*Ulmus sarniensis*). This is now quite often planted in streets and public parks, contributing distinction to the urban landscape.

Elms drop large branches rather more frequently and unexpectedly than other large trees. A fungal disease first described in this country in 1927, spread by beetles, seemed likely to devastate our elms. Fortunately, the damage done has now considerably lessened.

Instead, modern farming, which eliminates hedges, and power-driven hedging machines used without discrimination are causing a savage destruction of mature and young trees that is altering the landscape, and will be regretted in years to come. As a consequence, elm timber is already increasing in value.

The Beech

The typical beechwood is a localised and very distinct feature in the British landscape. Yet the beech will thrive and reach great size in many situations other than those in which we find these specialised woods – which lie on the chalk downs and the limestone formations such as those of the Chilterns or Cotswolds.

Beech will grow best in fertile, deep and well-drained loams with a good proportion of humus; it does not like cold, heavy soils. Yet in those hilly situations on which the beech 'hangers' form typical woods, the soil is seldom deep. The reasons for this are two. A young beech tree throws down a tap root which serves to anchor it. Subsequently, the root system, particularly if forced by the physical circumstances of its situation, develops near the surface. I have examined an old windthrown beech which had pulled up a mass of roots covering an area of some twenty-two feet diameter, yet the cavity left was only two feet deep at its deepest, while the diameter of the largest root broken was no more than two inches. Indeed: 'There at the foot of yonder nodding beech, that wreathes its old fantastic roots so high . . .' is no poetic licence.

It will thus grow on shallow soils into which trees such as the oak cannot drive the deep-delving roots that are essential for their nurture and establishment.

The other reason is that the leaves of the beech grow on a branch system that consists of an overlapping series of flat planes, thus preventing light reaching the forest floor. Any competing light-loving tree that does establish itself under a beech is quickly suppressed. This summer darkness accounts also for the typical flora of any beechwood, much restricted when compared with that under oak trees.

Two recorded examples will show how beech can be established on shallow soils when no other kind of tree will grow, eventually providing localised conditions under which numerous other trees may be grown to form richly wooded landscapes.

One is at Stourhead, where in 1741 a bare valley in a terrain like the neighbouring Salisbury Plain was planted largely with beech, as a beginning of the great landscape garden there.

We have more detailed information of the early days of another, more recent garden, now with a rich collection of trees and shrubs. In 1768 Admiral the Hon. Robert Digby bought Minterne in Dorset, then an area of bare chalk downland. On it he planted trees. Within a few years they were nearly all dead except the beech, which continued to thrive and gave the shelter and humus needed to establish an estate where today 'fine trees (of many kinds) can be seen that compare favourably with the best grown anywhere in the British Isles'.

The beech was a late arrival after the glaciated ages. It has been planted so widely for so many years that its precise distribution is difficult to work out. In general terms, it grew in south and east England and south Wales. Yet in 1548 William Turner wrote that two of the greatest trees he ever saw were in the hills above Morpeth Castle, Northumberland. Today it is a common tree, with many fine specimens, in the Lake District. Yet in 1675 John Worlidge, while describing well the typical situations in which we find beechwoods today, added, 'the tree is altogether a stranger to most counties in England'.

There were probably no pressing economic reasons for planting beech until comparatively recent times. It seems now to have been proved that many of our beechwoods, such as those on the Chiltern Hills, which were assumed to be natural, were in fact planted between about 1720 and 1850. The timber, though strong, will not stand exposure and has therefore no structural or outdoor uses. It can be bent and cleft, and traditionally is used for furniture making and turnery. It is not much affected by insects. 'Bodgers' used to work in the beechwoods and rough-shape the wood for the furniture factories. Other uses have been for moulds in brick-making and chucks for metal spinning. It is now also used for plywood.

The beech-nuts, or mast, provide food for animals and birds. In those years when there is a heavy crop, flocks of bramblings visit and systematically work through the woods; pheasants, too, eat the nuts, as do pigeons and mammals such as mice. We can assume that the use of beech for pig feeding would often assess their value in Domesday.

The 'kernel' of the seed contains the food, and is digested, and as the fruit is small and light, it is seldom carried far and accidentally dropped. It is therefore around the parent trees that seedlings are mostly found – perhaps because the beech, compared with an oak, is not a long-lived tree, and needs replacement close at hand.

The seed is rather oily, and no doubt because of our shortage of oil-producing nuts, an attempt was made in the eighteenth century to express this oil. It was the subject of a poem by Aaron Hill of 1715, *The Dedication of the Beech Tree* 'occasioned by the late discovery of making oil from the fruit of that tree'. It was to replace oil made from rape-seed in the wool trade: the nuts needed picking up only, in contrast to the elaborate cultivation and harvesting of rape. The timber, when dried, is good fuel, and was used in firing medieval glass, the residual ash also providing the alkali needed in the process.

The exceptional qualities of the beech that distinguished it in the landscape are two. The trunk, unlike that of most deciduous trees, does not carry incipient buds within any bark that is over some thirty years of age. Therefore, if an old tree is cut back, it will not 'break'. This lack of buds is indicated by the extremely smooth, pale grey, naked trunks of the beechwoods – quite unlike those of any other tree, except to some slight degree those of the hornbeams, which are markedly fluted – the beech being very circular (Plate 12).

Young trees can, however, be cut and will break to form hedges (which must be regularly clipped so that plenty of young, budding wood is present). At one time trees were pollarded, principally to provide fuel. Such are the famous Burnham beeches,[1] pollarded from about 1500 to 1820, when the use of coal became general; such, too, are the numerous pollards in Epping Forest.

Another distinctive feature of a beechwood is the persistence of the copper-coloured fallen leaves. Drifting into hollows, they cover deep pools of humus whose ruddy glow warms the woods on the coldest day.

The mature beechwood is, as we have already seen, almost always (and naturally) a mono-culture – certainly when growing on calcareous soils – in summer so dark that birds and other plant life are unseen, and of an even, tender green when coming into leaf.

The tree and shrub flora of the margins or open spaces of beechwoods is, however, of that delightful variety associated with chalk-land – guelder rose, wayfaring tree, spindle, thorn, yew, juniper, and orchis.

There are three distinctive 'sports' from the beech that are found in ornamental planting. The first is the form in which the red pigment is excessive, giving leaves a range from almost purple to copper. Few trees are more telling, or more frequently used, in ornamental plantings. It is a colour form that sometimes arises in nature. Seedlings from such trees include a high proportion of the same type. It was known at least as early as in the seventeenth century, when, in Switzerland, the first group of three trees arose (so it is said) on the site of a murder. It seems to have been introduced to England from an example in Thuringia some time about the middle or later part of the eighteenth century. Trees of over one hundred feet and twenty feet girth now grow in the British Isles. The differing colour forms have a variety of appropriate names, such as 'Atropunicea', 'Cuprea', 'Purpurea' and so on.

The fern-leaved beech, with variable narrow, often deeply-cut leaves, usually called *Laciniata*, is not nearly as common as the copper beeches, yet is by no means infrequent. It forms a large tree of the greatest beauty on account of the fine texture of its foliage. Its origin is unknown. It was apparently first grown here late in the eighteenth century.

There are, too, weeping and fastigiate beeches. The weeping beech was still an aboricultural novelty early in the nineteenth century; several variations propagated from weeping forms very rarely found wild are in cultivation.

[1] In 1955 the average age of the pollards was 320 years.

The fastigiate or Dawyck beech, 'Fastigiata', is finding its way into urban planting schemes. It was brought into cultivation by F. R. S. Balfour, who found a tree on his estate at Dawyck, Peebleshire, early in the present century. Earlier records of an apparently similar tree, however, exist.

The Scots Pine

We have in the British Isles but one native cone-bearing tree of forest size, the Scots pine. The area it covers in our woodlands is exceeded only by the oak.

Until comparatively recently it was generally referred to in the vernacular as the fir tree. Since botanists formed the genera *Picea* and *Abies*, now commonly called the spruce and silver firs respectively, and restricted the genus *Pinus* to those conifers having long, needle-like leaves which start their life bound into bundles of from two to five, to avoid confusion it is as well to substitute 'pine' for 'fir' in the case of this genus. *Pinus* was apparently applied in ancient times principally to the stone pine (*Pinus pinea*) whose fat seeds (*pignons*) are still eaten and whose large cones were symbols of fertility in the Mediterranean region.

The botanical name of this Scots pine, *Pinus sylvestris*, is rather puzzling when we learn that, botanically, *sylvestris*[1] means wild, as opposed to cultivated. One presumes that, as the Scots pine grows naturally in some of the same regions as the stone pine, which has been planted by man so extensively that its original natural distribution has been obscured, this fact explains the contrasted epithets.

The other amusing point about this tree is that though it has the widest natural distribution of any pine – it ranges through Europe from Scandinavia to the mountainous areas of the Mediterranean countries and into temperate Asia as far as Kamchatka, one will find that in, for example, an American book, the name Scots pine is still attached to it.

It came to us as one of the first immigrants after the period of glaciation. During the Boreal period it was the dominating tree over most of the British Isles, particularly the eastern districts.

During the age when the warm, moist Atlantic climate was prevalent, the pine disliked the conditions and was slowly driven north to Scotland by the spread of deciduous trees, which relished the new conditions. There still exist remains of these ancient southern pine forests. They can be found

[1] Another pine, *P. pinaster*, has a similar name; *aster* is a suffix with the same meaning as *sylvestris*. Neither this nor *P. pinea* are hardy enough to play an important part in the British landscape.

buried under the peat of the Cambridgeshire fenlands of, probably, a post-Bronze Age period. In Ireland it still grew in Neolithic times, and there are plentiful remains deep under the 'red bogs'. Ancient pine remains were found, too, among Roman remains in Suffolk.

There are today considerable areas of sandy land in, for example, Kent and Surrey, now densely covered with Scots pine, which there reproduces itself freely. Some authorities have suggested that these have developed over the centuries from small, isolated relicts of the original forests. It seems highly improbable, for historically it is known that pine was planted in these districts on a considerable scale during James I's reign – and now finds British conditions more to its liking than in ancient times.

Several references to 'firres' by the itinerant Leyland have been adduced to show that isolated patches of the old pine still remained in the time of Henry VIII. However, W. B. Yapp has shown that Leyland's references was almost certainly to furze, or gorse.

The native pinewoods of Scotland – now few and far between – have lately been much studied. They lie mostly in areas which have had the fortune to be inaccessible until recent times.

In the east of Scotland pine is found growing largely unmixed with other trees. In the wetter, western parts it grows mostly on the sides of and upon the tumps in the glens, usually mixed with birch. By nature it seldom climbs high up into the mountains, but on account of hardiness is frequently the first choice for planting at higher altitudes. It prefers light or gravel soils, preferably without lime content, but, when planted, is tolerant of a wide range of conditions.

The tree as it grows wild in Glen Affric (Plate 13), or the Black Wood of Rannoch (Plate 14),[1] forms some of the most picturesque and romantic natural scenery in the British Isles.

The Scots pine, with so wide a range, has developed a number of local races, each with distinctive qualities due to environment. Even within this Scots race, called *scotica*, it seems there are individual strains. Long ago, there was introduced seed from continental sources which had none of the qualities of the true Scots – hardiness and slow growth producing fine, tough timber.

In the eighteenth century the differences were argued, but somewhat

[1] From within the wood, the name is most misleading: the pinkish tinge of the old bark, the red of the top branches, the effects of the broken light and shade are full of colour. From across the loch, however, effects of light may throw the wood into sombre darkness.

inconclusively. They were made very manifest in the eighteen-sixties when Osgood Mackenzie was making his garden at the wind-swept Inverewe. He found the pines that he bought would mostly not stand the Atlantic gales, whereas trees from the 'old native fir-wood of Glaseleitir, on the shores of Loch Maree . . . are as different in growth and constitution from what are, alas! too often sold nowadays as Scots firs as Scots kale is from cauliflower'.

The eighteenth-century landscape poet Mason wrote:

> *The Scottish fir*
> *In murky file rears his inglorious head,*
> *And blots the fair horizon. . . .*

Before the century was out, the Rev. William Gilpin had set the record right, and at the same time put his finger on the very point that today's opponents of conifers misapprehend:

'The Scotch fir, in perfection, I think a very picturesque tree, though we have little idea of its beauty. It is generally treated with great contempt. It is a hardy plant, and therefore put to every servile office. If you wish to screen your house from the south-west wind, plant Scotch firs; and plant them close, and thick. If you want to shelter a nursery of young trees, plant Scotch firs: and the phrase is, you may afterwards *weed them out* as you please. This is ignominious. I wish not to rob society of these hardy services from the Scotch fir . . . all I mean is, to rescue it from the disgrace of being thought fit for nothing else; and to establish its character as a picturesque tree.

'For myself, I admire its foliage; both the colour of its leaf, and its mode of growth. Its ramification too is irregular, and beautiful; and not unlike that of the stone pine; which it resembles also in the easy sweep of its stem; and likewise in the colour of the bark, which is commonly, as it attains age, of a rich reddish brown.

'The Scotch fir indeed, in its stripling state, is less an object of beauty. Its pointed and spiry shoots, during the first years of its growth, are formal: and yet I have sometimes seen a good contrast produced between its spiry points, and the round-headed oaks and elms in its neighbourhood. When I speak however of the Scotch fir as a beautiful individual, I conceive it, when it has outgrown all the improprieties of its youth – when it has completed its full age – and when, like Ezekiel's cedar, it has formed its *head among the thick branches.*'

The practice of planting clumps of pine trees as landmarks brings out the qualities that Gilpin describes. Some are said to show that the planters had Jacobite sympathies, others to indicate to cattle drovers that here was a place where they could rest. Whatever the reason, these groups of trees, often on some eminence, play a distinct part in the landscape.

The Scots pine is likely to continue to take an important part in our woodland economy. Although it has not the speed of growth of other conifers, it remains an ideal tree for the poorer, light soils of the higher altitudes and exposed places. The timber, imported from the Baltic countries since early times, is strong and therefore used for structural work, telegraph poles, pit-props and joinery. For long the crop had as a disadvantage the valuelessness of the thinnings. Now these go to make wood pulp.

Pinewoods, particularly in the older, more open woods in Scotland, harbour a most interesting wild life. This includes the native race of crossbills, the capercailzie, the native race of the crested tit, the siskin and the goldcrest. When birch is present, the range is considerably wider.

As the extensive plantings of the Scots pine in the last few decades begin to mature and become like Ezekiel's cedar, the effect on the landscape is bound to be considerable – and full of interest.

The Yew

Until the planting of introduced conifers during the last two centuries, the yew, or 'English cedar' as Cobbett called it, was the only native member of the *Coniferales* (to which it botanically belongs, though its fruit is berry-like, and not a cone) to be found throughout most of the British Isles. It is also our only native evergreen forest tree, other than the Scots pine. It has, indeed, a long history with us, having been present before the period of glaciation and afterwards returning from the Continent when conditions improved, to become re-established before the sea cut the land bridge connecting Britain with the Continent. It has subsequently been so extensively planted, being readily adaptable to a large variety of conditions, that it is now difficult to define its true range as a British native tree.

But the districts in which it is regarded as spontaneous seem curiously to misrepresent its true requirements. Today it is found, for example, on chalk downs in southern England, on limestone rocks in Wales, and particularly on the limestone cliffs at Tintern. It will live in a dwarfed condition for many years upon a meagre diet when birds excrete the seed into some rocky crevice. A number of instances have been recorded; for example at Ludlow Castle, where there are a number of small trees growing high up in the walls, rather than on them.

Yet the essential requirements of the yew are an insular rather than a continental climate, which implies a moist, temperate atmosphere, and the absence of long spells of drought, cold and heat. Good drainage is also essential. One has only to 'feed' a yew hedge to observe how unnecessary for good growth is a sloping situation on limestone, and how much the plants prefer a rich diet to the hard conditions of cliffs or chalk hills: an 'old world' hedge can, indeed, be produced in a decade. Further proof of this was the discovery that many of the stumps of fen 'oaks', in that flattest of counties, Cambridgeshire, were actually the remains of yews – sometimes six feet in diameter and so hard that an axe bounced off them – which flourished in the fertile ground before waterlogged conditions arose.

The factors that result in the few pure British yew woods growing where they do must surely be those that inhibit other species reaching tree size in the same situation. Evidence that yews and yew woods were in early times as scattered as they are today is provided by the very few place-names incorporating Anglo-Saxon *iw;* they are most found in Kent, Hampshire and Sussex.

The age of yews has, since the early days of antiquarianism, received an undue amount of attention; systems have been propounded for calculating it according to the girth of the tree. But surely all are inevitably fallacious. For one thing, the speed of growth, and therefore the circumference, varies so considerably according to situation. Then a well-known feature in the growth of yews is that trees usually send up secondary stems from the base. These are not suckers, nor do they originally rival the trunk in thickness, but in time they encircle the main stem, so giving a false girth. Eventually the original trunk may die, and the ring of outer trunks merged together will, as it were, take over. The result is seen in such famous hollow yews as that at Much Marcle, or the lesser known one in the remote churchyard of Bacton, both in Herefordshire. They differ from hollow trees of other kinds in that what remains is not the outer bark and live part of the original trunk, whose heartwood has rotted away, but a series of new, minor trunks circumferential to the original. It must be said, however, that this form of growth is not universal, and occasionally old yews with an unencumbered single trunk exist.

Scientific examination of the age of ancient yews is rarely possible, not only for the above reasons, but because trees must be felled to count the rings. In 1926 A. S. Watt, on the basis of ring counts, fairly confidently assessed the age of the oldest yews at Kingsley Vale at seven hundred years. Yet in 1954 one of the reputedly ancient Closewalk Yews at Midhurst in Sussex was found to be only three hundred years old; its health had deteriorated noticeably during the present century.

Yews certainly have a tenacious hold on life. An example is the famous Buckland yew, near Dover. In 1834 it was described by the Rev. W. T. Bree as of great antiquity; he relates that in the middle of the eighteenth century it had been shattered by lightning. This catastrophe had a remarkable effect on its appearance. Mr Bree wrote: 'Imagination, indeed, might readily trace a fanciful resemblance between this vegetable ruin and some anatomical preparation of an animal trunk, of which the viscera displayed, and preserved entire.' By 1880 the head of the tree had grown so vigorously that it pressed too closely on the church, and in that year William Barron, most redoubtable of tree movers, transplanted it bodily, with complete success.

The most curious thing about the yew is that, although it has been associated with our churchyards for centuries, no one really knows why (Plate 15).

It is interesting to review the suggested reasons, with the warning that Dr Vaughan Cornish, after studying the subject with immense thoroughness, came to no very definite conclusions. He did, however, produce a map showing that old churchyard yews were much more common to the west of a line drawn from, roughly, Chester to Plymouth, with the heaviest concentrations in Wales and its bordering counties, Devon, Somerset and Dorset. He linked this with early population densities – though this also coincides with the climate and conditions most suited to yew. He showed too, that old yews were always younger than their churches.

Was the yew required in funeral ceremonies? Evelyn, that great lover of ancient authorities, can produce no more than that Statius so implied in *Epicedium Vernae*. (Apparently this obscure author was a Portuguese poet named Estaçao, who died as relatively recently as 1581). Nor can such a custom be traced to the Roman invasion, as has been suggested, for the yew, owing to its truly poisonous leaves and the allegedly mortiferous nature of its shade, was execrated by classical authors. I can trace no record of yew timber having been found in Romano-British burial sites.

Was it planted as 'some symbol of immortality, the tree being so lasting and always green', to quote Evelyn again? There is no evidence that this was so; the not unusual literary comparison of yew with the Mediterranean cypress does not, I believe, occur before the late sixteenth century and only becomes common in the seventeenth.

Unfortunately, modern studies of the earliest churches give no confirmation to the belief that the connection of the yew with churches, or even places of worship, is of great antiquity. The early churches of Northumbria of A.D. 400 to 800, it is said, were neither monastic nor evangelical. They were essentially open, and presumably treeless, protected clearings, places for peaceful contemplation. Though I have searched such writings of Bede (673–755) as are available in a form understandable to the ignorant, I have not found any reference to the yew.

On the more practical side, there seems no reason to dispute Evelyn's claim that he introduced yew as a 'succedaneum to cypress, whether in hedges or pyramids, conic spires, bowls, or what other shapes'. For instance, in the *Parliamentary Surveys* of the famous gardens at Wimbledon in 1649 and of Theobalds a year later, which go into minute details of the trees and hedging plants, yew is not mentioned once.

Was it later planted in churchyards to provide bowstaves? There is no doubt that yew was held in high esteem for this purpose, but there is a tendency to overlook the fact that old authors name other timbers, from Giraldus Cambrensis in the twelfth century with his 'wild elm'. Against this theory, too, is the fact that only the bole – not the branches – of clean-grown yew stems can be used for staves. At the beginning of the last century, a Mr Waring, 'the first bow manufacturer in England, and perhaps in Europe', informed J. C. Loudon that there was no yew wood left in Europe fit for bows, so high was the necessary standard. That trees casually grown in churchyards could achieve this quality is surely impossible. Even at the beginning of the fourteenth century, as is shown in N. S. B. Gras's *Early English Customs Systems*, large quantities of bowstaves – of unspecified timber – were imported.

It is, perhaps, not widely known that yew has a much earlier connection with man's lethal activities than its use in the bow. From it was fashioned the oldest recorded wooden artefact – a spear found in an interglacial deposit at Clacton-on-Sea; another was later discovered in Lower Saxony, embedded in the ribs of the now extinct straight-tusked elephant. May we not rashly hazard a guess that, since the yew is generally found scattered and localised, it was planted at some communal meeting spot, such as that where religious rites were held, so as to be readily available, and where its poisonous leaves would be out of the way of stock? And that from this tradition evolved the placing of yew trees in churchyards as a ready source of its timber?

However much we may speculate upon the origin of ancient yews, we have no need to do so about the Irish yew which, since Victorian times, has almost replaced the common kind in churchyards. Probably every one of these is descended from a sport found in the mountains of Fermanagh, of which the Earl of Enniskillen distributed cuttings in about 1780 from his seat, Florence Court; for that reason it is sometimes called the Florence Court yew.

The original tree, which still stands, is female; that is, it 'burns lamps of peace' alone, and does not carry the pollen-scattering male flowers. Because a few male-flowered trees otherwise identical with the Irish yew have been found, it has been suggested that these had another origin. There is no evidence to support this view, and as the common yew sometimes bears flowers of both sexes, it is possible that this sport occurred in a Florence Court yew.

An instance of both sexes occurring on one tree was seen in the original West Felton yew, perhaps the most remarkable of all yews. Preponderantly male, this tree produced a spray 'exuberantly profuse in female berries, full, red, rich and luscious'. From this branch most of the trees of this kind have been propagated; the seeds invariably produce only the common sort.

This comparatively little-known variety is exactly the opposite of the Irish yew in every way: 'with a single aspiring leader to a great height, each branch in every direction dangling in tressy verdure downwards, the lower ones to the very ground, pendulous and playful as the most graceful birch or weeping willow; and visibly obedient to the feeblest breath of summer air' is the flowery, but not inaccurate description of the tree written by J. F. M. Dovaston, the nineteenth-century poet, antiquarian and musicologist, whose father acquired it in a manner not unworthy of a fairy tale. John Dovaston came of a family that had lived at West Felton, near Oswestry in Shropshire, since Elizabethan days; he was without education, but of 'unwearied industry and ingenuity'. Having sunk a well, he found that the sandy soil was continually slipping back into the shaft. To prevent this, he proposed to plant a yew tree, having observed the close mat formed by its roots. In about 1776 he purchased a plant for sixpence from, of all fairy-tale people, a cobbler. The tree not only fulfilled its purpose, but Grimm-like grew into the unique tree which botanists call *Taxus baccata* 'Dovastonii'. They thus not unnaturally honoured the planter, rather than the cobbler.

On very rare occasions most kinds of tree produce a seedling with some abnormality, such as the erect and pendulous growth of these two yews. Particularly in townscapes the erect forms are today quite often planted. The original example, if left to itself, would in time disappear, for its seedlings will almost invariably revert to the normal growth. The existence of these strains, now usually called cultivars, is therefore dependent upon some observant person segregating and propagating them by vegetative means – that is, by cuttings or grafting. It is quite unusual, except in recent times, to know the life stories of these exceptional trees whose genes have for some reason behaved so eccentrically.

Finally, there is one forgotten use of the yew that still affects the village landscape in a minor way – being in most cases a memorial of the past. It was first brought to my notice by B. A. Box, rather incongruously in his study of English parsonages, and is easily confirmed by observation. 'Jericho, or the Necessary House, or the Bog House, as Warr called it in 1765', frequently stood under a yew tree, which both screened and to some extent protected it from climatic extremes.

The Ash

The ash, *Fraxinus excelsior*, is scattered throughout our woodlands and countryside. Except when planted, pure ashwoods are uncommon. It is the last native tree to come into leaf and the first to become bare; the rhyme about the relative leafing of oak and ash prophesying the summer weather being, therefore, without substance. In some years, however, the precocious flowering of the ash, always on the naked twigs, and always before the oak leafs, gives a misleading impression of foliage.

Few trees are more heavily encumbered with folklore. In Scandinavia Ygdrasil, the tree of the universe, was an ash. The tradition still persisted until the last century that no adder would pass through a circle of ash boughs. Twigs from a tree in which an unfortunate shrew was imprisoned had surprising therapeutic qualities.

The ash was probably most abundant during the moist, warm climate of the Atlantic period. It has a wide geographical range, comparable with the oak, with which it often grows, the ash only predominating when the lime content of the soil rises above a certain value. In the north of England this results in pure ashwoods such as are unknown elsewhere.

The keys bearing the seeds, having mostly hung on through the winter, are scattered by the March winds. They lodge, besides on woodland soils, in crevices such as those found in the limestone 'pavements' in the bleak

13. Scots pine growing with birch; Glen Affric, Inverness.

14. Scots pine beside Loch Rannoch, Inverness.

15. Centuries-old churchyard yew; Peterchurch, Herefordshire.

16. Aged ash; Bolton Abbey, Yorkshire.

17. Ash; Manifold Valley, Derbyshire.

18. The moisture-loving alder; South Staffordshire.

19. The tower-like white willow; Cradley, Herefordshire.

20. The spreading crack willow; South Stafford-shire.

Yorkshire moors, as near Malham Tarn, or in ruined stonework. A fine example of this being the great tree at Bolton Abbey (Plate 16). Yorkshire is indeed good ash country, for the tallest, 148 feet high, is in Duncombe Park, near Ripon. It is often seen in the limestone dales typical of the north, as in Derbyshire (Plate 17). Equally good trees grow on sandy loams farther south.

Coppiced poles of the tough, light, flexible timber have supplied since ancient times the perfect spear shafts, or, more pacifically, the handles of tools. Ash provided the framework of light horse-drawn vehicles, next of early automobiles, then finally of the first aircraft. Today its greatest value is, when of suitable size and quick growth (not easy to obtain), for sports goods such as tennis-racket frames and hockey sticks. It also provides veneer and plywoods.

The weeping ash, often planted in Victorian times, is propagated from trees very occasionally found in nature. A famous source in the eighteenth century was a tree found by the vicar of Gamlingay near Wimpole in Cambridgeshire. Another occasional freak is a form with the number of leaflets, usually eleven, reduced to three or even to one.

The Minor Trees

Of trees that are particularly localised owing to ecological reasons – that is, their distribution is restricted because they only grow freely under certain conditions of soil or situation, the alder (*Alnus glutinosa*) is the commonest (Plate 18). The need of this tree, as any observer of the landscapes must have noticed, is plenty of moisture. It also dislikes shade, and is therefore most frequently seen stretching in more or less single file along stream-sides. The form is distinctive, the crown being narrow, with short, spreading branches. Gilpin called it the most picturesque of our water-side trees excepting the weeping willow. It is found throughout the British Isles, in southern Scandinavia, throughout Europe, and spreads into Asia and North Africa. It is therefore a very adaptable tree and somewhat variable. In the British Isles, for example, it varies by a reduction in leaf, catkin and fruit size as it moves from south-east to north-west. The alder arrived here in the Pre-Boreal climate of 8000 to 7000 B.C. and increased steadily. It has decreased as a consequence of drainage and the reduction of woodland. Here and there woods of pure alder remain in Scotland, Wales and around the Norfolk Broads, where it forms what are named 'carrs' (which were several times painted by J. S. Cotman).

The use of alder timber has been killed by the universal adoption of the

D

wellington boot. As it is tough and does not decay when continually wet, it was used for the soles of clogs. The 'cloggers', often a family which had been in the business for generations, would buy an area of alder. They would then move in, erecting tents in which they carried out their work, but did not live. The best trees for their purpose were thirty feet or rather more high, with a girth of sixteen to twenty inches. With a special saw a felled tree was cut into lengths, then split, and finally shaped. The trade needed skill, which took several years to acquire. The wood was suitable because it was non-absorbent when dry, was worked and shaped easily, and would take many nails without splitting.

The other important use of alder was as the source of the charcoal from which the old black gunpowder was made. It is still used to some extent for charcoal making, and is now also being used for the manufacture of chip-board.

The long crimson pollen-bearing catkins extending and becoming lax in February or early March decorate the scene and give a cheering hint that spring is on the way. The female flowers form small, woody, cone-like containers for the seeds, which are released in large quantities in late winter. They are so constructed as to be buoyant, and they can often be seen in the course of their distribution floating down streams in myriads. When a pool is frozen, a strong wind may bring them down in such quantities as to cover patches of ice.

The dialect names for the alder, still in use in many districts, of owler and aller, take us straight back to the Old English, *alor*. The old Scandinavian *elri* is found in such place-names as Ellerbeck.

There is little folklore involving the alder, though I know an old lady who in her youth was advised by woodmen on the farm never to burn 'aller' as the Cross was made from it. She told me it made excellent firewood.

In Germany, however, the *erlenbaum* seems to be associated with unpleasantness. For example, the terrifying poem of Goethe, *Erlkonige,* set to even more horrifying music by the teenager Schubert.

A small tree, usually seen as a solitary specimen, yet spread widely over the British Isles, is the rowan or mountain ash (*Sorbus aucuparia*). The description of Gilpin (though he believed it to be a form of the common ash) cannot be bettered, for both accuracy and its appearance: 'Its name denotes the place of its usual residence. Inured to cold and rugged scenes, it is the hardy inhabitant of the northern parts of this island. Sometimes it is found in softer climes: but there it generally discovers by its stunted growth, that it does not occupy the situation it loves. In ancient days, when superstition held that place in society, which dissipation and impiety now hold, the mountain-ash was considered an object of great veneration. . . . Its chief merit now consists in being the ornament of landscape. In the Scottish highlands it becomes a considerable tree. There on some rocky mountain covered with dark pines, and waving birch, which cast a solemn gloom over the lake below, a few mountain-ashes joining in a clump, and mixing with them, have a fine effect. In summer, the light green tint of the foliage; and in autumn, the glowing berries, which hang clustering upon them, contrast beautifully with the deeper green of the pines; and if they are happily blended, and not in too large a proportion, they add some of the most picturesque furniture, with which the sides of these rugged mountains are blended.'

This sturdy yet slight tree is spread over Europe, as far north as, but not within, the arctic zone, and in the southern parts as a mountain tree, west Asia and Siberia. It has become naturalised in North America. In Britain it grows up to an altitude of 3,200 feet – higher than any other tree, and exceeds fifty feet in height on rare occasions.

Superstition has left it but slowly. I have seen a sapling, alongside one of birch, placed with utmost seriousness on either side of a cottage door on May Day. In Scotland, shepherds would make their sheep pass through a ring made from its branches.

The berries have one disadvantage. They are liked by birds and disappear as soon as they are coloured. This liking is the origin of the word *aucuparius*, which means a decoy for birds. They have a high vitamin C content. In Norway the fruit is relished by bears, and the bark is a favourite winter food of elk. John Evelyn remarked that though the tree had no practical use, as long as the berries last you will be sure of the company of thrushes. The name rowan comes from *raun*; the Old English Witchen and Quicken have long been local names.

The rowans (several, mostly from China, are now being planted in our gardens and parks) have pinnate, ash-like leaves. A second type of *Sorbus* has entire leaves, and the commonest is the white-beam (*S. aria*). This small tree is one of great beauty. The leaves, particularly when young, are almost white below. The dense clusters of heavily scented, hawthorn-like cream flowers, immensely attractive to insects, are delightful. The large fruits are scarlet. Except locally, particularly on chalk or limestone, where it may grow in some numbers, it is not a common tree, and cannot be said to enter, except as an individual, into the landscape.

Another native sorbus is the wild service (*S. torminalis*). The leaves are unlike those of the rowan or the white-beam. They are deeply lobed. It is a very uncommon tree, yet scattered all over the countryside except in the north of England and Scotland. It is small and only enters the scenery when smothered with creamy-white flowers in May or June, or the brilliant red and yellow leaves in autumn. The fruit is brown and drab.

An anomalous position in the landscape is taken by the field or hedge-row maple (*Acer campestre*). It is a trimmed hedgerow shrub in certain parts of the countryside, and then its flaming autumn colours, often combined with those of spindle and guelder rose, and draped by old man's beard, are outstanding. Yet, on its own, it is a shapely tree reaching seventy feet or more. It is found principally in the midlands and the south and south-east of England, being particularly noticeable on limestone formations. It is not a native of Ireland and rare – possibly only introduced by man – in Scotland. It has a wide distribution in Europe southwards of Scandinavia, spreading into western Asia.

The name maple, of Old English origin, comes from *mapuldor*, and is not common as an element in place-names, being limited in accordance with its natural distribution. It does not enter into folklore. The wood was used throughout Europe from early times for mazers – shallow, metal-rimmed drinking vessels. These were turned from the large burrs almost always found on the boles of old trees. It is not commercially cultivated: the figured 'bird's eye' maple is usually imported.

Two willows enter the landscape scene, one, the white willow (*Salix alba*), with considerable significance among our lush water-meadows (Plate 19). There it either curls along with the water-course in the form of pollards, or elsewhere rising (quoting H. Gilbert-Carter) 'to form a magnificent tree with a rather narrow outline and square head somewhat resembling a church tower'. The undersides of the leaves are white, the upper green; when, in high summer, a breeze ruffles the tree, it becomes almost blue.

The poles cut from the pollard once had many uses for fencing, and as stakes and hurdles. They were cut leaving their stumps to form a level top (so that the new shoots would grow erect) at a height of eight feet or so from the ground to prevent stock from damaging the new growth.

The white willow is a native and was apparently an early arrival. Yet it is rarely, if ever, seen as a self-sown tree. It is native of a wide area ranging from south Norway and north Russia southwards to North Africa, spreading outward to the Himalayas.

It is propagated by driving stout shoots, called setts or truncheons, into suitable ground. A number of hedgerow trees have resulted from poles being used for hedge stakes while still live. A distinct type, the cricket-bat willow, has, during the present century, become a feature of some parts of the country; it is planted in rows, pruned and felled at an early age, from fifteen to twenty years.

Another variety, *vitellina*, with young twigs which are bright yellow, is quite often seen, and locally is very noticeable in the winter landscape.

The other native willow that grows to a large size is the crack willow (*Salix fragilis*). It has wide-spreading branches, sometimes making a sprawling tree, and green leaves (Plate 20). It also is seen as pollards along stream sides, and is commoner on the poorer soils. Sometimes considerable patches are found in more or less derelict damp land. As the name implies, the twigs break away with little pressure and often root where they fall. This tree has much the same natural distribution as the white willow. Locally, several other willows are grown to provide osiers, and small, but scarcely tree-like willows are found in many wild places.

The willows are closely related to the poplars. We have only two native species; the several other kinds now cultivated came into the scenery at a later stage.

The native black poplar – the epithet black seems never to have been explained – is a variety of the wide-ranging *Populus nigra* restricted to western Europe. It has been called the East Anglian poplar with some justification, for its very individual form can be recognised in the paintings of Constable. It is a large tree with a few heavy branches, some of which arch downwards. The trunk usually bears large burrs. It was at one time planted in parks beside rivers and lakes, probably because of the great beauty of the long crimson catkins of the male tree, which are often showing in March. Today, except in East Anglia, it is not a common tree, but arresting when in flower.

Nor is our other native poplar, the aspen (*Populus tremula*), found in all parts of Britain (Plate 21). It is rare in the south and east. In the west and north it is found forming suckering thickets, not infrequently being one of the first trees to establish itself in felled woods, particularly high up on hills. The aspen is normally native on poor soils and is a small tree. On better soils it reaches fifty or sixty feet. The trunk is smooth, the crown slender. The leaves turn rich yellow in autumn. The tree is not generally conspicuous in the landscape, but known because of the ever-rustling leaves. The unkind words of Patrick Hannay written in 1622 are an apt description:

> *The quaking aspen light and thin,*
> *To th' air light passage gives:*
> *Resembling still*
> *The trembling ill*
> *Of tongues of womankind,*
> *Which never rest*
> *But still are prest*
> *To wave with every wind.*

In Britain the tree is of no economic importance. In Scandinavia the timber is used for making match-sticks.

The hornbeam (*Carpinus betulus*) is a native tree with an even more restricted distribution, principally centred on south-east England, but often planted elsewhere. It is one of the few trees that will thrive on chalk. From early times it has been grown pollarded or coppiced, along with oak. Many of these trees are now neglected, and have grown into gnarled, fantastic specimens, with smooth grey bark much like that of a beech, but easily distinguished by the deep fluting of the bole. The leaves turn a bright yellow earlier than the beech. The seeds are held in a distinctive dagger-shaped bract. In the landscape it is not prominent unless one is within a wood where it abounds. Trees in such places are often several centuries old, for when coppiced it has a much longer life than if grown naturally.

Used as firewood, it gives a hotter flame than any other timber, burns slowly and produces a very pure charcoal. The name 'horn' indicates another of its qualities, hardness. From it were made the teeth of gear-wheels and other mechanical parts, long since made from metal, and it has been used as a hedge.

A solitary specimen in a park, gracefully pendant, interesting in flower and fruit, lovely at leaf-fall, is on occasion seen, and may reach sixty or seventy feet.

Two of our most beautiful native trees, the small-leaved lime (*Tilia cordata*) and the large-leaved (*T. platyphyllos*), are rarities. The lime that is so often grown is a hybrid between the two (*T. vulgaris*) and was probably introduced from the Continent in the sixteenth or seventeenth century. This will be mentioned later in our history. The absence of the species is surprising, as during the warm and moist Atlantic and Boreal periods both were common trees in our woods. Possibly, as oak became more and more dominant and the climatic conditions changed, it was gradually choked out. Under cultivation, fine trees of both exist.

The broad-leaved lime is still found apparently wild on limestone formations on the Welsh Borders and in South Yorkshire. The small-leaved seems to have a similar distribution. There exist the remains of woods of both, particularly the small-leaved. They produce timber that is most often seen in intricate wood carvings. Possibly the small-leaved was grown and coppiced for charcoal. There would be other uses for this easily-worked, reliable timber if the limes had not been allowed to disappear. The fibres of the bark at one time supplied the bast used for tying, and weaving mats. It would be pleasant to see a revival of the use of limes in forestry, for particularly when, in early July, they flower and are sweetly scented they are delightful trees. Probably today they would provide valuable timber for plywood, for during the Second World War it was much used in Mosquito aircraft. Anglo-Saxon place-names based on *lind* and *line* suggest that in post-Roman times it was a relatively common tree, and would contribute to the then valuable honey crop. The timber was also used by the Anglo-Saxon warriors for the orbs of their shields.

Of our minor natives, none is more conspicuous in winter than the holly (*Ilex aquifolium*), one of our only three evergreens. In Britain it grows in many situations, from within woods (it will tolerate shade) to rocky situations on mountain-sides, where it will grow at 1800 feet. It is believed to have been an immigrant during the Boreal period. It is found in most of western Europe and in the Mediterranean region, where it is usually a mountain tree. It is commonest in western and southern parts of England and in Wales, becoming rare in the extreme north. It is surprising that, though a persistent native, holly can be badly damaged or even killed in a severe winter. Also puzzling is the fact that though the berries are supposedly the food of birds, who distribute the seeds, frequently – and not only in mild winters – they remain on trees far into the following summer. The use of berried sprays at Christmas time (or its former equivalent) goes back beyond Christianity.

Holly in field hedgerows and holly hedges round gardens are an important part of the country-garden scenery; Evelyn praised the latter three centuries ago. In mixed hedges by farmyards, hollies are often trained up as standards. The reason for this is not, as is sometimes believed, superstition. The holly tree is dioecious, that is, the male, pollen-bearing flowers are always together on one tree, the female flowers that produce berries on another. These standards are almost always berry-bearing and as such may well produce a saleable crop of berried holly.

A minor point that the curious have remarked upon, at least since the time of John Aubrey in the seventeenth century, is that holly is often associated with ancient iron workings. Aubrey, too, was one of the first to remark on the existence of yellow-berried trees.

Gilpin summed up the holly so: 'Though we cannot accord with the learned naturalist (Evelyn) in the whole of his rapturous encomium of the hedges at Sayes Court; yet in part we agree with him; and admire, as much as he does, the holly, glittering with its armed and varnished leaves; and blushing with its natural coral. But we could wish to recommend it, not in a hedge, but in a forest; where, mixed with oak, or ash, or other trees of the wood, it contributes to form the most beautiful scenes; blending itself with the trunks, and skeletons of the winter; or with the varied greens of summer. . . . In many situations it appears to great advantage: but particularly growing round the stem, as it often does, of some noble oak, on the foreground; and filling up all the space, to his lower boughs. In summer it is a fine appendage; and in autumn its brilliant leaf, and scarlet berry make a pleasing mixture with the wrinkled bark, and heavy moss, and auburn leaves of the venerable tree, which it incircles.'

The ivory-white wood of the holly, of exquisitely fine texture, was used for veneer and inlay. From it were once made most finely-toothed hair combs. Dyed, it is a substitute for ebony. In the days of horses, slender branches were used for whip handles. From ancient times bird-lime was prepared from the bark: apart from catching birds it was used to protect the stems of trees and plants from slugs, snails, caterpillars, rabbits and hares.

The old English name *holegn*, also in the later form of *holme*, is an element in place-names scattered widely over the country.

Two native cherries on occasion attract attention in the scene. The larger and more conspicuous is the gean (*Prunus avium*), a gaunt-limbed tree that on occasion reaches ninety feet; in May it is Housman's 'cherry hung with snow', and in autumn so flaming in colour that no poet has attempted to describe it.

This cherry, one of the ancestors of our cultivated sweet cherries, is found all over the British Isles, though rarely in northern Scotland.

It is usually found in oakwoods, particularly on limestone soil; in the Chilterns it is a notable sight among the beechwoods. The gean has a wide range, covering most of Europe, northern Africa (on mountains) and western Asia. The fruit, as the name *avium* implies, is quickly eaten by birds which scatter the stones far and wide. Surprisingly, cherry (unlike most English tree-names it derives direct from the Greek; gean is of French origin) does not enter into place-names. Does this suggest that its abundance is comparatively recent, arising as seedlings of the cultivated cherries in our orchards?

Our other native is the bird-cherry (*Prunus padus* – the latter being an ancient name). It is very distinct and is a small tree noticeable in the landscape only when in flower during May, and then for the most part only in the hill woods and hedgerows of Scotland, northern England and Wales. The flowers are white, very small, and in narrow spikes.

In former times, scattered among the rough grounds and scrub, growing probably to a greater size than we see now, would be the crab, elder and blackthorn. The bullace and 'wild' plums and pears that we now have would not be present.

The crab apple (*Malus sylvestris*) would be found growing in oakwoods and scrub; it has a wide distribution over the British Isles, with the exception of central and northern Scotland, often growing at well over a thousand feet on hillsides. Many of the 'wild' crabs found today are, however, seedlings of cultivated forms with a complex parentage. It has a wide native range, growing over most of Europe and spreading into south-west Asia.

The fermented juice of the crab provided verjuice or vergess, the equivalent of vinegar. The timber was used for ornamental work.

The elder (*Sambucus nigra*) would, both in flower and fruit, have been as prominent as today, perhaps more so, for, in Jason Hill's words, 'whenever you find it growing freely you may be sure that you are not among restless, meddlesome people, since no tree invites pruning more flagrantly, or yields to it more easily.' It is, indeed, often treated as a weed and therefore seldom allowed to reach tree size. It is capable of girthing over three feet and reaching thirty feet. It has a wide distribution, covering all the British Isles except the north of Scotland, and ascending up hills and mountains to 1,500 feet, and a frequenter of a great variety of situations, including the shade of mature conifer plantations. It is found in most of Europe, spreading to western Asia, north Africa and the Azores.

It is difficult to account for the legends of malevolence that surround this tree. Well into the present century a taboo on it existed. In Hampshire as recently as the nineteen-forties, and possibly later, forest workers who had cleared it from the woodlands would burn neither it nor rubbish in which it was present. The reason is that the Cross was made from it (elder does not grow in Palestine). And then, it must be remembered, it was one of the several trees upon which Judas hanged himself. Miss Jekyll was told by her country neighbours that its roots must never be allowed to grow into a well, or the water would be spoiled.

On the credit side, in some counties the women-folk kept witches from the house by making signs upon the floor with bruised elder leaves; in the sixteenth century if elder twigs with bruised leaves were used to whip vegetables they would be free from caterpillars.

Folklore in some places also demanded that an elder should be saluted by raising the hat when passing by; curiously, it is recorded that the Dutch botanist Hermann Boerhaave (1668–1738) subscribed to this rite.

The elder is of no economic value. The hollow branches are (or perhaps were) valued for pan pipes: Pliny advised that the best for this purpose are those cut from a tree that never heard a cock crow. The flowers and berries are used in elderberry wine. One might also include as an aesthetic benefit the belief that young goldfinches taken from an elder bush and caged sang better than any other kind.

All this, surely, tends to show that the elder has since time immemorial had an intimate association with man. Today it makes its most singular effect on the landscape of industrial waste heaps when heavy with cymes of white flowers in late June and July. It is, along with certain sallows, the first small tree to colonise such desolate places.

Finally, two evergreens – of which we have so few – the box (*Buxus sempervirens*) and the juniper (*Juniperus communis*), which are normally shrubs, but do on occasion reach the form and size of trees. One or two boxwoods exist on the oolite and chalk of southern England. There is argument over whether these are part of the native forest or have spread from Roman introductions. If they are native, then the natural distribution is discontinuous, for it is not present except as a planted shrub in France. Also, remains of its wood are found in Roman burial sites.

CHAPTER TWO

From the Celts to Medievalism

THE WOODLANDS ATTACKED

WHEN THE SEA had severed us from Europe, changes in our land surface continued. Mankind, our tiny population, would have seen these, and today evidence of a number is still available. One form is the submerged forests. The remains of their stumps can be seen in several places. In the Bristol Channel, off Lydstep in Pembroke, a Mesolithic or perhaps early Bronze Age pig was found with a tree-trunk across its neck, man's implements also being present. In the peat of East Anglia ancient tree stumps come to the surface owing to a complex process of shrinkage of the peat. Oak, yew, pine, alder and birch are found – oak being the commonest, though many examples originally believed to have been that tree are now found to be yew.

As the land sank – good, fertile land able to sustain trees – drainage failed and peat formed. In time the trees died, became insecure, and as often as not slowly toppled over under the influence of the prevailing wind.

It seems to be the present opinion that these major coastal changes ceased at the beginning of the Christian era. Some authorities adduce from the discovery of water vole remains in the pellets of birds of prey in Bronze Age barrows on Salisbury Plain that water was then regularly available for these creatures much nearer at hand than the present five miles distance to the River Avon, but this can be disputed. Avalon, the site of Glastonbury Abbey, was then literally an island among marshes.

That these changes continue to this day can be seen in many industrial areas. For example, within living memory the River Tame in South Staffordshire, a pleasant, fertile vale less than a century ago, has sunk and become waterlogged, the oaks first becoming stag-headed and then dying. Equally, elsewhere the water-table has fallen, because of water extraction, excessive drainage, and river clearance. Little attention appears to have been given to these long continuing changes in the distribution of our woodlands.

Early man often settled on the hills, with the consequence that he began his assault on the woodlands from above. As has been mentioned, our earliest artefact is a yew spear, and there is later evidence to show that the wood was much favoured for this purpose. In view of the comparatively recent discovery of the high proportion of yew in East Anglia's sunken forests, it may be that this lethal timber was more freely available than today, and in sizes large enough to make bows as well as spears.

The early settlers cannot have made much impression on our forests. The forests, on the other hand, impressed the Celts. They had gods of oak and beech. Sacred trees, woods and groves, the home of tribal deities, are recorded. Personal names connected, in particular, with yew and alder are known. Tree forms, however, were not used in Celtic art.

Place-names from the centuries before the Romans still remain to remind us of the woods of those early times, particularly in what have been called the peripheral parts of our islands, where the archaic heritage of the Celts has remained a direct factor of language and nationality throughout historic times. Their name for oak, *derw*, like the names of other major natural features outside these areas, has remained unchanged through many centuries.

With the arrival of the Romans, change, if only of a transient nature for a mere four hundred years or so, came to parts of our islands with a vengeance. Further, as users and builders in stone, as erectors of innumerable memorials which can still be read, and droppers of great quantities of the more imperishable forms of litter, they left so much history on and just under the ground that first the hobby and now the profession of antiquarianism has thrived on it for a couple of centuries.

The Roman accounts of our forests and trees are, however, sparse, and unreliable. The study of Roman remains gives us much evidence of the change in water-levels, which, as has earlier been mentioned, must have played a singular part in the continual change in the nature of woodland. The most obvious is the number of Roman wells that have long been high and dry and well above the water-table. At Verulamium, under the floors was found a species of marsh-living worm still eking out an existence in what is no longer marsh.

We must therefore assume that the woods that the Romans saw occupied much higher land than they do at present – a fact that was confirmed a few centuries after they left.

Probably their most significant effect on the woodland was the felling of timber to provide fuel for their considerable mining undertakings. Tin in Cornwall, copper, lead and gold in Wales, iron in the forests of Kent and Sussex and Dean, salt in Worcestershire and Cheshire, all must have resulted in destruction of trees. There were, too, potteries. The towns, forts, villages and even villas would have consumed very much more fuel – particularly when we recall the lavish use of hot water – than ever the natives had used.

Main roads mostly followed the firm, dry land as, for example, did the Fosse Way from the River Axe to Lincoln, nearly all of which is on the limestone ridge, except where, to achieve straightness, it drives across what was the dense oak woodland of Warwickshire. This road making, involving clearance for forts and stations, was still on such a comparatively limited scale that the total effect was small. Mining, too, was very localised.

The Romans were the first to introduce hydraulics into our country and thus to make use of wooden pipes. Their existence is confirmed today by the remains of the iron collars used for the joints. It is known that the manufacturers could bore an elm trunk at the rate of thirty-eight feet per day, the hole being two inches in diameter.

The Romans were great agriculturists, and it seems fairly certain that they introduced a number of trees. At Silchester remains of the fruits of medlar, plum, and damson, all of foreign origin, were found, as were, most surprisingly, the black mulberry – now believed to have originated in the mountains of central China. From their perishable nature, it is difficult to believe that they were not locally grown, rather than transported from the Continent.

There is some doubt whether they introduced, or cultivated, the walnut – a tree particularly associated with Rome. Godwin gives the date of introduction as 'late post-glacial'. I have, however, never seen any recent reference to the discovery of nuts from Roman sites (this tree is discussed later). On the other hand, many remains of the edible seeds, *pignons*, of the stone pine, *Pinus pinea*, have been unearthed. Unlike the perishable fruits, it seems improbable that these were produced here. This umbrella-topped pine, so well known in paintings of the Italian landscape, is rarely – in spite of its historical interest and great beauty – seen in this country; it is not generally hardy. The presence of these edible 'nuts' is explained by the use of the cones for altar fuel in the temples of Mithras; this religion at one time played an important part in Roman civilization. The thirteenth-century naturalist Bartholomew Angelicus wrote: 'Pinea, the pine apple, is the fruite of the pine tree . . . [it[is the most greatest nut, and conceiveth in itself instead of fruite many kernels, closed in full hard shales.' These exceptional qualities caused the Mithraists to choose it as a religious symbol, presumably of fertility. Particularly in the north, whole 'pineapples' are found on Roman sites – not real cones, but images of them made in stone or terracotta – usually in the form of finials. The showmanship of this religion was well managed. At the innermost end of the temple Mithras himself, accompanied by two torch-bearers, Cautes and Cautopates, was within a sanctuary. Skilful illumination heightened the drama of the scene, while sacred fires burned upon the altars, filling the building with the pungent smoke of the smouldering cones.

On looking at the map of Roman Britain, one is immediately impressed by the ramifications of their road systems, first for military or administrative purposes, and secondly to reach outlandish mineral deposits. And then one realises the great areas remaining untraversed and without settlements. The Romans can have impressed themselves but little on the woodland of the country in which they settled.

After the Romans left, we are faced with a period known as the Dark Ages, lasting some eight or nine hundred years. The darkness is due to the fact that the persons concerned, until towards the end of their time, were not disposed towards putting things down in writing, and unlike the Romans, they built largely in timber. The remains of their buildings are therefore extremely difficult to trace and until recent years have not attracted antiquarians, but the latter have, lately, with the aid of aerial photography and other scientific ingenuities, shed a little light in the darkness, and, incidentally, shown that the later Anglo-Saxon chroniclers were not such romancers as was long generally believed.

It has been said that with the coming of the settlers there began a series of changes in land utilisation of great importance which has continued until today. By degrees agriculture spread from the more easily worked soils of the river valleys to the heavier soils from which the scrub and forest were cleared.

It seems that, unlike the stone-built Roman settlements, whose situation was dictated by the proximity of stone, the Saxon settlements were often close to dense woodland.

Aerial reconnaissance was responsible for the excavation, under B. Hope-Taylor, of one remarkable Anglo-Saxon building site, that at Yeavering, in Northumberland. This great palace, begun in about 547, lies among the now treeless Cheviots, and made lavish use of timber-framed construction – oak and possibly ash were used. The place corresponds with the Gefrin of Bede.

In the first stages heavy baulks, shaped by an adze, were used. Finally a lighter construction of planks became general. Does this suggest that the timber was becoming exhausted, that it had to be fetched from lower levels, down by the river?

Another problem arises. It has been suggested that there were columns in this palace surmounted with the goat as an emblem. The place of the goat in these early communities does not seem to have been studied. If it was domesticated on any scale might it not have made, by destroying young growth, the first disafforestation caused by man's animals? The desert that can be produced by goats is well enough known in the Mediterranean regions.

The long, narrow buildings of this period are suggested by the few stone churches that remain (generally built of stone pillaged from Roman ruins), such as Brixworth, Deerhurst and Earls Barton. It is apparent that the design was conceived in terms of timber rather than stone.

The Anglo-Saxon centuries cannot have contributed to any great change in woodland, other than its destruction, but as they progressed the general scene must have altered considerably. Many of the large Roman stations and towns fell into decay. Instead there were developed the numerous small settlements so often the origins of villages, even the towns and cities, of today. Each village settlement was enclosed within a fence of thorns or more probably of pales.[1] The agricultural economy was based on corn, therefore the most valuable ground was the arable land. There were also the meads, usually by streams, producing hay, and the leas, uncultivated open land used for rough grazing, represented today by village commons. The shortage of grazing land severely limited the number of stock that could be wintered.

The neighbouring woodland was valuable, apart from the timber it supplied for building and fuel. Villages without any close at hand usually possessed some elsewhere – one cause for subsequent detached areas of

[1] The hedges that we know today – and for that matter the stone walls – apart from parish boundaries, are mostly the result of enclosures, particularly in the eighteenth and early nineteenth centuries.

parishes. In very densely wooded districts it was necessary to surround the village and its cultivated ground with a strong fence, the *haga*. The forests beyond this had two assets for the community. First was its value for pasturing swine (later known as pannage), and second as a game preserve. The pig for long played an important part in woodland history; with its powerful snout and teeth it rips up and eats the succulent roots of the woodland plants throughout the year. Slugs and similar enemies of germinating acorns are also a part of its food. In autumn, the fall of acorns, beech nuts and similar fruit (the mast) fattens the pig for slaughter – as one of the most completely consumable and easily preserved beasts – in November. Though it eats great quantities of acorns, it also tramples many into the ground, safely hidden from jays, mice, squirrels and other creatures who would otherwise consume them.

The significance of trees in this Anglo-Saxon civilisation is shown indirectly in two ways. First, place-names. These were descriptive, and many still survive. The number of 'thorns' has already been mentioned, from which the deduction can be made that a village was outside the dense oak forest. There are many place names based on *ac* and its forms – the oak. These would be within the oakwood area. We have today, for example, Accrington, Acklam, Acle, Acomb, Acton (sometimes used in combinations such as Acton Round, Acton Trussel), and modernised forms such as the several Oakleys, and Okeover. Birch, too (as one would expect), is a fairly common element, deriving from *beorc*. Bartlow, Berkley, Berkhamstead, Birkdale and Birkenhead are examples. It is still usually easy to see the significance of *alor*, alder, that tree of wet places, in Aldridge, Aller, Alrewas, Arle, Ellerbeck, Ollerton and Orleton. And so one may continue. *Aeppel*, apple, and its forms *apuldor*, *appletre* and *aeppeltun*, are frequent; *aesc*, the ash tree, is common. There are *boc*, beech (a little puzzling this, and liable to confusion with other rather similar elements with different meaning); *box* and *byxe*, the box tree, are, as would be expected, not common; *ellern*, elder tree, also a word that may be confused with other elements; *elm* and *wice*, elm trees, are similarly perplexing; *haesel* and *knutu*, hazel-nut, are quite common; *holegn*, holly, or in the form *holme*, is not infrequent; *lind*, the lime tree, is not common and may be confused with *lin*, flax; *mapuldor*, field maple, is surprisingly uncommon; *pirige*, pear, is sometimes greatly distorted, as in Bultsbury, said to mean 'Botwulf's pear tree'; and *plum* or *plyme*, plum, is a common element. There are a few places evolved from *raun*, mountain ash. *Withig*, willow, in the form of this old word that gives us withy, is liable to be

21. The quaking aspen; Falls of Rogie, Ross and Cromarty.

22. Remains of coppiced wood of small-leaved lime; Sharawley, Worcestershire.

23. Remains of a medieval chase; Cannock, Staffordshire.

24. Salvator's tree; the sweet chestnut.

confusing; Hoarwithy, for example, is held to be whitebeam. Willow in its bush form, sallow, from *salh*, is more reliable. *Iw*, yew, is uncommon, but straightforward.

The English geographical etymologists perplex us by claiming that *saeppe*, spruce (the modern French for spruce is *sapin*), found in names such as Sabolen (spruce valley) and Sapley (spruce wood), may be in reality pine. This seems rather doubtful.

Other words having their origins in this period have interest. *Beam* is tree. *Holt* is a wood (still found as an element in place-names). *Hurst*, when associated with trees, is usually a wood or copse. The terminations *-ley* and *-laugh* are common elements, particularly in old forest areas. They indicate a grove or thin clearing in a wood or forest. The termination *-shot* was probably used in the sense of untilled land overgrown by trees. *Tree* gives us a common second element in the forms of *-tre* and *-try*, the first usually indicating some special tree.

Of singular interest are the land charters. These are documents delineating the boundaries of grants of land, which often coincide with present, or past and recorded, boundaries of parishes. R. J. Stonor in his history of the ancient Buckinghamshire house and estate whose name he bears, translates from a charter of 774 the passage: '. . . so to the small ash tree and then to the maple tree on the west side of the valley of the Ass'. An ash still stands at the same spot – no doubt a descendant – and is still the boundary mark.

Many of these charters have been translated and annotated. Some, no doubt, are late copies and even forgeries produced to justify claims, and one does, perhaps, feel a little more suspicious of them than their learned editors. But that does not invalidate the general conclusions that can be drawn from the surveys that accompany the charters. These are the importance of individual trees, groups of trees and woods in the later Anglo-Saxon period as features of the landscape, and their use as landmarks and the determination of boundaries. We may take G. B. Grundy's study of Worcestershire charters as representative. Such phrases as 'from the Black Pit to the Thorn Thicket', 'between the Two Woods to Alder Brook', 'up along the Severn to the Combe of the Lime Trees', are common. The references to individual trees shows their importance as land and boundary marks.[1] For example, in the survey of Stoke Prior, near Droitwich, through which passes the little Salwarpe stream, we read

[1] Until the last century, such trees still played their part in the ancient ceremony of beating the bounds.

'from the Lea to the Service Tree . . . from the Service Tree to the Rugged Maple Tree', and later, 'from the way to the White Birch Tree . . . from the Birch Tree to Alcherd's ford . . . from the Salwarpe River to the Ivy-covered Oak . . . from the Oak to the Boundary Oak'.

It is not easy to find the precise number of trees of the different kinds mentioned, as the same tree may be mentioned twice. Thorns predominate. In addition to references, such as those already quoted, to thorn thickets, there are named some twenty-three individual thorns or numbered groups (for example, 'two thorn trees' and 'four thorn trees'), such as 'Lal's thorn', 'broad thorn', 'great thorn', and 'thorn tree of earth nuts'.

There are twenty references to oaks, such as 'five oaks', 'three oaks', and 'black', 'rugged', 'crooked' and 'tall' oaks. The apple tree has seven mentions: 'hoar apple-tree', 'twisted apple-tree', and 'spreading apple-tree' are instances. The lime tree makes five appearances, though, except for the common lime, not introduced until centuries later, it is now a rare tree. However, it was recorded as recently as a century ago that there were aged specimens of *Tilia cordata* still existing in Worcestershire.

Willows and pears are mentioned four times. Although the pear is a dubious native, this shows the tree whose fruit is now displayed in the county's arms was a very early introduction.

Birch has three references, ash and maple two. Aspen, service tree (*Sorbus torminalis*) and holly appear only once. Alders are mentioned, but not individually.

On ecological grounds one would expect neither pine nor hornbeam. The rowan, yew and elms are missing. The former is not a remarkable tree, the yew today is found either in urbanised centres or in woods. The elm is now the 'Worcestershire weed' along the hedgerows – is this an indication that in the county it arrived rather late, perhaps during the age of enclosure? All these trees, with the exception of the small-leaved lime, would still serve as mark trees – the aspen and service tree on account of their comparative rarity. Seven or eight more trees now recognised by most people could be added to the list today. One or two, possibly, were rarities brought by the Romans, others were not known here until centuries later.

Finally, it is now generally held that the great forests of the Normans – the vast areas of land held sacred to the chase – had their origins in the later years of the Anglo-Saxon rulers.

In 1066 we were once again invaded and conquered. It is as well to remember at this stage that from early times south-eastern England was 'very definitely a part of Europe and has never been entirely isolated from the main current of European affairs'; with the coming of William I this connection became much more intimate. John Harvey put clearly a fact that is now usually overlooked. When Henry II, born in Anjou, came to the English throne in 1154, through his inheritance and by marriage he ruled over a land of great contrasts stretching from the Cheviots to the Pyrenees. Through it ran a great cultural artery from Narbonne, Perpignan and Montpelier in the Mediterranean through Carcassonne to Toulouse and then to Bordeaux. This led to developments that considerably affected our woodlands and usage of timber.

For our purpose, the first point of interest of the Norman invasion is the production of the famous survey called Domesday Book.

In the first place, it may be well to demolish a popular misconception about this undertaking. It is not a survey of boundaries, and therefore does not, as local legends often claim, mention individual trees.[1] It was, briefly, a survey to find out who owned the land, what it produced and what it was worth. For this purpose, it was necessary to give areas, their usage and such other simple facts somewhat comparable with a modern examination of productivity. Woodland, with its many uses, was therefore included.

This undertaking, carried out by the precursors of our modern civil servants, is often acclaimed as a great achievement. In practice it was nothing of the kind. Its ambiguities, lack of standardisation of reporting, the muddles of its co-ordinators at headquarters (for example, local reports were mis-sorted and attributed to the wrong counties), have kept a whole army of interpreters active down to the present day, without anything more than speculative conclusions resulting.

So far as woodlands are concerned the survey has, for obvious reasons, a major omission: the royal forests are excluded, and any references to them are incidental.

We are a little better off when we come to other woodlands. Their value was principally assessed by the number of pigs that they could feed, the fuel and charcoal they could produce, and in some cases their honey rent. Little is said about timber value. The feeding and fattening of pigs seems, from its frequent mention, to have been the most important.

In Domesday, therefore, the woodland is often assessed in terms omitting area, but giving only the number of pigs that it will support. Experts on occasion have tried to convert this into acreage. In Bedfordshire, for example, a ratio of $1\frac{1}{2}$ statute acres to each head of swine was

---

[1] It is not beyond the realms of possibility that these traditions are really linked with Anglo-Saxon boundaries.

evolved. Unfortunately, this or any other figure ignores the variable nature of woodland. Durmast oak produces far fewer acorns than pedunculate. Oak and ash woodland would support fewer pigs than either; beech mast is light and intermittent. We just cannot provide a pig/acreage ratio.

Even so, when measurements are given they are often utterly confusing, and are usually inconsistent. It is interesting to quote a few examples.

In Lincolnshire details of woodland are classified under two headings, *silva pastilis*, woodland proper, and *silva minuta*, and are given either in acreage or linear measurements of leagues by furlongs. The pannage figure is also mentioned. In Norfolk and Suffolk the number of swine supported is almost universally given; one Norfolk wood seems to have been exceptional in that it would support 1200.

In Cambridge we are given swine numbers, except in certain districts where the estimate is based quite unusually on the sufficiency of wood suitable for fences, building and fuel. In Huntingdonshire the measurements cannot be understood and in Gloucestershire terms of length and breadth are used, but they are difficult to interpret.

The Welsh border counties were in a peculiar situation, particularly Herefordshire, where villages ravaged by the Welsh quickly reverted to woodland; for Pembridge is the puzzling entry of a 'wood for 160 swine if it had borne mast'.[1] By 1086 woods had grown up on village land that had been sacked in 1055. It is in these border counties that the value of honey produced in a wood was important, a survival of Welsh economics – the value was in the wax.

Worcestershire has one interesting entry. The Bishop had all its proceeds in hunting, honey and timber (*Lignis*) for the salt pans at Droitwich.

Terms for different types of woodland used in addition to those quoted above include *silva infructosa*, perhaps wood not having mast; *spinetum*, thorny scrub; *silvula*, underwood; *nemus*, which survives in botanical Latin in the form *nemoralis*, of woodland, and *fraxinetum*, an ash spinney.

Of the Norman forests and forest-law, much is known and much has been written. A forest was quite distinct from woodland, and had from late Saxon times the very distinct definition of woody grounds and fruitful pastures privileged for wild beasts and fowls of forests, chase and warren to rest and abide there in safe protection of the king, for his delight

---

[1] Woods in Warwickshire and Northamptonshire also bear the qualification 'when they bear mast'. This might indicate durmast oak or, less probably, beech.

and pleasure. The term forest originally had no connection with trees. It is from *foris*, without the common law.

Thus, by means of savage laws, great areas of the country were preserved more or less in their virgin condition. That these royal forests were covered with dense woodland is a misapprehension of their nature; deer and game – let alone huntsmen – need open space and grazing.

This is not the place to discuss the law and customs of these forests. Perambulations were later made from time to time of their boundaries and duly recorded, and there is plenty of information about them in more recent times.

The Earl of Cardigan, hereditary Warden of Savernake Forest, has described its history. The forest area reached its maximum in about 1200, after which, like most other forests, the acreage declined, by piecemeal reclamation.

East to west, at its widest part, from East Kennet to Hungerford, it was about fifteen miles wide. North and south, from Ramsbury to Collingbourne, it stretched for nine miles. It covered about one hundred square miles. The woodland was not extensive (a map of 1301 shows only seven large areas of wood) and was interspersed with rough, uncultivated land well suited for the preservation of game.[1]

It is estimated that during the eleventh and twelfth centuries, when forested land was at its greatest extent, the laws covered one-third of England. Thus, not for the last time, sport provided a rough-and-ready preservation of huge areas of the countryside from agriculture and every form of intrusion and development.

Throughout the middle ages much dense woodland remained. The existence of post-Domesday place-names such as those with the element *leah* (clearing) is one indication, for example, of the dense wood that for long spread from around Burford into western Buckinghamshire; Wychwood Forest included large areas of woodland until the middle of last century.

On the other hand, there was in many places a reduction in the number of swine that woodland would feed, not because of assarting (clearance for use by grubbing up stumps), but because of the activities of charcoal burners and by the sale and gifts of timber. Such partially devastated land did not speedily return to woodland, but remained as waste. At a later

---

[1] The present appearance of Savernake bears little likeness to the original forest. It results from planting begun in about 1720, when the present 'ancient' beeches were planted.

date, the Black Death must have had the same effect. Then, as now, neglected land, even when adjoining woodland (except in a few areas), goes through many decades of the varying stages of scrub before good trees even begin to show some domination.

E. A. Kosminsky has summarised the economics of the demesne, that is, the lord of the manor's woodland, in the thirteenth century. Revenue came from several sources. There was the sale of timber, brushwood, deadwood, hedge or heybot (wood or thorns for the repair of fences), housebot (wood for the repair of houses), and of smaller items such as nuts.

The income from these was not paid to the lord item by item. Rather, a levy was paid by the manorial tenants for the right to participate in a share of them. On occasion, however, there were larger items of income which may have come from more extensive felling.

There seems often to have been a regular system of woodland management. For example, the brushwood was cut annually in a fixed proportion.

The woodland and assarted land belonged to the demesne, not to the village. One result of this was that it was a long time before the assart became part of the open field system.

The royal forests have already been mentioned as areas in which woodlands were largely protected from disturbance in the interests of sport. There were similar areas, decreasing in size, which were the sporting province of social grades less than royalty. Next in standing to the royal forest was the chase, a minor forest on the estate of some powerful and influential landowner, such as a bishop or an earl (Plate 23). Third came the park, a part of the demesne lands of the lord of the manor. This was an enclosure of wild land suitable for game and sport. The fencing consisted usually of an earthen bank, sometimes with a ditch within,[1] surmounted by a fence, usually of pales – sometimes a stone wall or thorn hedge – which was only broken by a 'deer-leap', which enabled deer of the three kinds, red, fallow and roe, to enter, but not leave.

Unlike the forest and the chase, which were areas with defined boundaries, the park was securely fenced to prevent the escape of the beasts once they were within it, and to impede the entrance of those not entitled to take game – who, as in forests and chases, were liable to substantial

[1] Surely this was the ancient principle upon which the ha-ha was based. Sport was not the only asset of owning an enclosure for deer. Their food value, including salting for winter, was appreciable, for they were far more self-supporting than cattle.

penalties if they were caught poaching. Many traces of these parks remain today. The earth banks may sometimes still be traced, the line of the original park pale may still dictate the line of present hedgerows and field boundaries. Place-names embodying 'park' often, but not always, relate to them. The actual type of wooden paling, which can be seen in contemporary drawings, may still be seen around some parks, having been kept repaired in the traditional manner by succeeding generations. One example is at Charlecote Park in Warwickshire.

An indication of the extent of these parks can be gained from L. M. Cantor's study of the medieval parks of South Staffordshire. In the area of the county south of Stafford, between the Conquest and the Dissolution, he has found evidence of thirty-nine parks. They were scattered fairly evenly over the land, except within the areas of the royal forests. The creation of parks was at its height between 1200 and 1355 – the period when the royal forests began to decline.

The final and smallest form of sporting right was the right of free warren, which was not a form of enclosure, but granted the owner the right to hunt the smaller game. Presumably, it would not greatly affect the status of woodland.

Early in medieval times we first come across the presence of the rabbit, or coney. It was an introduced animal, and by the sixteenth century was regarded as a nuisance in gardens and orchards. One can only assume that in this country predators were then so numerous that the rabbit had no chance to prevent the establishment of young trees as it was to do in the nineteenth and, particularly, twentieth centuries.

During the middle ages, and, as will be mentioned, long afterwards, rivers played a major part in internal transport, and it can be assumed that the first inroads on massive growing timber were in those districts accessible to water. L. F. Salzman quotes as an interesting example the case of the important port of Lynn, which could be reached more cheaply by water than by any other means from the counties of Warwick, Leicester, Northampton, Rutland, Bedford, Buckingham, Huntingdon and Cambridge – a striking contrast to later years when railways, unlike some of our greatest rivers, ran only north and south. He refers to one instance bearing this out. In 1229 the king granted oaks to Richard de St John from Sherwood Forest for house building, with instructions that they were to be cut as near to the River Trent as possible for carriage to Norfolk by water.

Salzman and other writers on medieval trade cite examples of imports of timber mostly from Scandinavia. Although our country was so richly wooded, and we could build some of the finest ships in the world, we had nothing in light and reasonably strong, straight lengths such as the stems of pine and spruce grown in the north. As early as 1297 Godfrey Pylerin of Yarmouth went in his ship *Dieu la Sauve* to buy masts. His fellow burgess Robert Wyth also sent boats to Norway for them in 1297 and again in 1300. In 1305 the *Cristofre* sailed from Yarmouth for the same purpose. English masts were probably at that time, and certainly within the next century, composite structures ingeniously made from a number of pieces of timber.

Mention has already been made of the effect of the Cistercian economy on our woodlands. In addition, John Harvey describes how the greater consumption of our most massive timber came about at this time. The demand for larger buildings was restricted by the problems of using more and more massive stone vaulting. The answer was found by the structural carpenter, who devised a variety of trusses capable of spanning large areas, lighter and far easier to erect than any masonry. The effectiveness and longevity can be seen in many examples that survive. The material used was oak. Most exceptionally was chestnut employed, in spite of statements to the contrary. Oak was then freely available in large sizes, but even so records show that on occasion long and tedious search was made for trees of exceptional size for particularly demanding structures. Oak was still in such plentiful supply that there was enough for the building of several thousand monasteries, churches and manor houses, with plenty over.

MEDIEVAL INTRODUCTIONS

With the development of monastic culture and its interest in plants, we are on safer grounds in discussing three trees which for centuries have held a prominent place in the British Isles, but about whose introduction there is much doubt. Taking the woodland and numerically most abundant tree first, the sweet or Spanish chestnut (*Castanea sativa* or *vesca*) is most perplexing. Owing to extensive cultivation in areas where it is not native, and its ability to reproduce itself within them (it does so in England), its natural northern boundary is difficult to define. It is, however, a native of France. There are those who suggest that it was a pre-Roman introduction, but the evidence appears slender. Certainly the Romans would have

25. Walnut in the village of Powderham, Devon.

26. Sycamore in Sulgrave churchyard, Northamptonshire.

27. Wintour's Leap, near Chepstow, commemorating a legendary jump over the Wye in 1664 by Sir John Wintour, despoiler of Dean Forest.

28. A larch wood, Herefordshire.

29. Lime avenue; Castle Howard, Yorkshire.

30. Norway spruce; Paddock Wood, Kent.

31. London Plane; Lincoln's Inn Fields.

32. Lebanon cedars; Exbury, Hampshire.

known the tree and valued its nuts; there are a very few satisfactory examples of traces of the tree in Roman remains – which do not, however, conclusively prove that they established the tree in this country. The Anglo-Saxons came from districts where it does not grow. The first undoubted record of its cultivation is in Dean during the reign of Henry II. It is significant that in 1548 Turner makes no mention of the tree, which at least suggests that it was then a comparative rarity.

There are extremely aged specimens in this country which may give us a hint in solving the problem. The most famous is the hulk, still alive, of the tree at Tortworth in Gloucestershire – which may now well be three trees coalesced so as to appear as one. It was first described, rather inaccurately, by Evelyn in 1706. He obviously based his account on what he had been told. He states that it stood 'upon Record' as a boundary tree in the time of King Stephen. It seems impossible to substantiate this claim. But the fact remains that this tree existed as a most remarkable aged specimen at the end of the seventeenth century. We know that trees planted about that time, or rather earlier, now rank as distinguished trees, attracting attention today. Therefore, we can safely conclude that the Tortworth tree was, when Evelyn described it, at least three centuries old, which would take us back to 1300, and suggest that the tree from its presence in a remote district, though not far across the Severn from Dean, was by then not a rarity.

The timber of the sweet chestnut has the same general qualities of oak, with the additional advantage that it is far more resistant to insect attack. Unfortunately, however, the trees are very subject to 'shake', a fault in the structure of the timber making it valueless in large sizes. For this reason, beams reputed to be chestnut in old buildings can usually, but by no means always, be shown microscopically to be of oak.

The remarkable, and now most valued, feature of the chestnut is that, when cut hard back, it produces a number of coppice shoots. At about ten or twelve years old these have developed into strong poles with an unusually high proportion of heart-wood, giving them great strength. The timber is also very durable in the ground, and these poles were, and to some extent still are, used to support the many acres of 'wire-work' which support the hops. It so happens that chestnut thrives in those same areas in which hops are grown. The other merit of chestnut timber is that it splits (or is cleft) easily and straightly into lengths ideally suited for the pales of fencing. For this purpose it is still in great demand.

It has long been grown for coppicing underneath widely spaced standards of oak, providing regular crops of poles during the long period that the oak takes to mature.

As, at the time the chestnut was introduced, there was plenty of better timber available, one can only assume that it was brought here because of the food value of the nuts to both man and beast. In some years these are produced in great quantities, and numbers of self-sown seedlings arise from the midlands southward. It is not impossible that in southern and south-eastern England it would maintain itself without man's help. Today, the nuts are imported from the Continent, produced by selected strains.

The natural range of the tree is from France, south-west Germany and Austria, to Algeria, Asia Minor, the Caucasus and west Persia. In England, trees have exceeded one hundred feet in height and thirty feet in girth. Large specimens have been recorded from as far north as Edinburgh.

In the English landscape, woods of pure chestnut have a distinctive purplish-grey sheen. In July they turn greenish-white from the millions of narrow spikes bearing minute flowers.

Grown individually, or in small clumps, it had a close connection with the English landscape movement. Its aesthetic qualities in this connection were summarised by Gilpin: 'in maturity, it is a noble tree; and grows not unlike the oak. Its ramification is more straggling, but it is easy, and its foliage loose (Plate 24). This is the tree which graces the landscapes of Salvator Rosa. In the mountains of Calabria, where Salvator painted, the chestnut flourished. There he studied it in all its forms, breaking and disposing it in a thousand beautiful shapes, as the exigences of his composition required. I have heard, indeed, that it is naturally brittle, and liable to be shattered by winds; which might be one reason for Salvator's attachment to it.'

Unlike the chestnut, the walnut is very rarely a forest tree. It is its majestic presence neighbouring thousands of old farmsteads – even cottages – and in many gardens and orchards that makes an impact on the landscape (Plate 25).

Godwin states that it was introduced in late post glacial times – a little vague. As it was well known to the Romans, surely they would have grown it here. Pliny wrote that the tree was first brought out of Persia at the command of kings, and therefore known as Persian and royal nuts (adding that the oil drawn from the kernels was a singular cure for baldness). As is well known, the nuts played an important part in Roman marriage ceremonies. The tree was later promoted to even higher status when it was given the name *Juglans*, a merging of the words *Jovis* and *glans* (nut), thus attributing it to the Emperor of the World. Linnaeus clinched matters by using the epithet *regia*, royal. One is surprised that though pine nuts have survived from Roman days, there is apparently no record of walnut shells.

Etymologists inform us that our name walnut is evolved from *wealh*, meaning foreign: that is, a nut brought – perhaps by the Romans – from far away, as distinct from the common hazel nut of northern Europe. This name was probably not coined in England, but introduced from the Continent, not, however, from France, where it is *le noyer*.

The walnut has been cultivated over so wide an area for so long that there is some difficulty in defining its natural range. In 1568 William Turner wrote that it was 'well known in all countries'. In 1670 John Ray wrote 'that though it does not grow wild among us or perhaps elsewhere in Europe . . . we may regard it as naturalised if not indigenous'.

The tree must have been here a considerable time to have become so common. Certainly, the nut is mentioned in Aelfric's Latin Anglo-Saxon Glossary of about the year 1000. This does not, however, prove that it was grown here – merely that it was known. Presumably the most important reason for introducing it to England would be to express the once valuable oil from the nuts. We were very short of oil-producing vegetables.

The earliest record of the tree being actually cultivated in this country is a quotation by M. Beresford. During a feud between the inhabitants of Willstrop in Yorkshire and a local landowner, the villagers in about 1498 smashed a fence and 'hewid and kit doonn 100 walnottreis'. That the nuts were then the most valued product of the tree is shown by references between 1503 and 1508 to 'barellis' of 'walnotts' being imported into Kings Lynn.

The timber in due course became of more value than the nuts, which in Britain have long been used almost entirely for pickling before the shell has hardened. In view of the substantial plantation at Willstrop we may, perhaps, assume that numerous articles of 'walnuttre' were made from home-grown timber. In 1603 Lord Bruce, coming south from Scotland, brought with him 'one wallnot tree tabill', and John de Critz, the artist, who died in 1642, decorated a 'wallnutt tree' bed in gold and purple for the palace of Whitehall.

The use of home-grown walnut timber was considerable before the great vogue in the early eighteenth century. Evelyn in 1664 wrote that our cabinet makers preferred the Grenoble trees,[1] though adding that there

[1] Possibly because the valuable burrs are seldom produced in Britain.

were a number of walnut plantations in this country. He names that of Sir Joseph Child at Wanstead as the largest, and others in Surrey and Kent. Even so, the Earl of Haddington wrote in about 1732 (he was then planting at Tyninghame, near Dunbar), 'I think the walnut the most valuable tree we have that sheds its leaf. Had we this tree in greater plenty, the furniture of our houses, such as chairs, tables, bed steads, etc. that are commonly made of beech, would be much handsomer, and more durable. Besides, it is much sought after by cabinet makers, so that I wish it were more propagated.' By then, a number of landowners besides the Earl were making plantations, and those that Evelyn mentioned were no doubt taking their profit. For, besides furniture making, the trade for gun-stocks was rapidly increasing the value of the trees, which was raised still further by the devastation of the walnut woods of Switzerland, France and Germany in the dreadful winter of 1708. It was not a totally ill wind, however, for Loudon tells us that Dutch merchants were astute enough to buy the dead trees which they later sold at great profit. A century or so later the Napoleonic campaigns caused the price of the timber to soar once again. By the eighteen-thirties fantastic prices were being paid – one fine specimen fetched £600. The gun-makers of Birmingham, then the greatest source of fire-arms in the world, imported large quantities, principally from Italy and Germany. The Crimean war came next, and our own supplies being insignificant, one Birmingham firm built a sawmill at Turin, which eventually converted about 100,000 trees into 3,000,000 blanks for gun-stocks.

Lack of foresight lost us both the profit and our walnut woods, which must have been a magnificent sight. In the last few decades, the high value of the timber, now used for veneer, has caused the felling of very many of our finest trees, but has, fortunately, resulted in the formation of some plantations.

The walnuts of our countryside are so connected with an old rhyme that it should be mentioned:

> A woman, a spaniel, a walnut tree,
> The more you beat them, the better they be.

This is not the place to discuss the adequacy of the claim as it concerns the first pair in the trio. As to the tree, the fruit used to be knocked down with long rods, before the rooks and squirrels took it. A vigorous, thrashing movement was used, which at the same time broke the long, sappy green shoots and encouraged the production of short, fruiting twigs.

One of the trees most frequently seen in practically every part of the

British Isles, particularly on hillsides around farms and in equally windy places by the sea-shore, is the sycamore (*Acer pseudoplatanus*) – still often called plane in Scotland (Plate 26). This is also probably a medieval introduction. It is rarely planted in our forests in any quantity, but is often found growing in them, for the most part having arrived by chance.

The sycamore presents us with a number of puzzles. First, it is the only tree, except perhaps the horse-chestnut, introduced by man that has, with little help from him, spread and become naturalised in practically every part of the British Isles, all within four hundred years. It seems to be the only introduced tree that increases in numbers of its own accord, and might well, if man ceased to inhabit Britain, establish itself as part of our permanent flora, the winged 'keys' carrying the seeds far afield.

The original home of the sycamore was the mountains of central and southern Europe, but it has been planted so widely that there is some disagreement over its precise natural range. It is, as its behaviour in this country shows, an extremely hardy tree. The precise date of its introduction is problematical. The leaf is clearly carved on the shrine of St Frideswide, Christ Church, Oxford, 1282. One can only assume that it was done by some itinerant mason, or imported. The first mention of this tree, as a native of the mountains on the Continent, particularly of Germany, with no mention of its presence in England, is in Turner's *New Herball* of 1562. Gerarde in 1597 remarked that it was a rarity in England. There is evidence to show that it might have been introduced to Scotland during the fifteenth century; in that country it was a constituent of woods by the middle of the seventeenth century. By the late eighteenth century it was becoming naturalised in England. The white odourless wood was used for dairying vessels, butter casks and similar purposes. The tree was also planted for shelter.

An insoluble puzzle – at least so far – is why it is known as the sycamore. The sycamore has for long been the name of *Ficus sycomorus* (sycamore fig), the tree up which Zacchaeus climbed to see Christ. In no way has *Acer pseudoplatanus* the slightest physical resemblance to that tree, though it has a slight likeness in leaf to the common edible fig, *Ficus carica*, which was grown in this country in the mid-sixteenth century. Equally perplexing is its old connection in Scotland with 'dool', or mourning trees.

A likeness of leaf to that of the plane tree is obvious, the difference being that the leaves of the sycamore spring from the twigs in pairs, those of the plane alternately. The bark of the trees is very different. The sycamore's is grey and is scaly, but does not peel off as does the plane's, and often has a subtle, pinkish tinge.

77

The compact, rounded, richly-textured deep green head of the sycamore, particularly when seen on the northern limestone hills, is a significant feature of the landscape.

The timber, especially if it has an ornamental grain, is now greatly valued for furniture and similar purposes.

CHAPTER THREE

Tudors and Stuarts

SPOLIATION

DURING THE SIXTEENTH CENTURY the quantity of wood used in the iron industry began to increase considerably, an increase that continued into the eighteenth century. Wood was used for two purposes, for melting the iron and for producing charcoal. From the time of Elizabeth I the production of coal increased steadily, but charcoal was still needed for the 'charking' or 'coking' process in the production of iron.

One of the first large increases in demand for Wealden iron was brought about by cannon founding. In 1545 Peter Bande, a French founder of brass cannon employed by the king in London, and Ralph Hogge, under the superintendence of Parson Levett, cast cannon for the first time in iron. For some two centuries after, the English had an almost complete monopoly of this industry.

As the century progressed, with the increasing use of the blast furnace introduced from France, and improved methods of iron smelting, the 'iron mylls' began steadily to 'decaie, spoil, and overthrow woods and principal tymber'.

In some areas where the use of furnaces had been long established, there was a regular system of coppicing on a fifteen-year rotation. This was not so with the new generation of iron-masters. The first Lord Paget set up in 1550 at Teddesley, Abbots Bromley and Cannock with a full licence from the Crown 'to use as coal for making iron' all the 'timber trees of oak, ash and beech growing thereabouts'. Within thirty years all the timber left on Cannock Chase would not, reported the Surveyor of Her Majesty's Woods, yield over £1000.

When Henry VIII came to the throne, though demands for timber were steadily increasing, there were, if sound silviculture was practised, abundant supplies in our woodlands, many of which were still scarcely accessible for exploitation. In 1536 the monasteries were suppressed. In addition to the Cistercians, the other orders held considerable areas of woodland which were managed on the traditional system. When the priors and abbots realised what was impending, many began cutting immovable timber to turn into movable cash. Shortly after the suppression, the royal agents cut the saleable timber for the benefit of the exchequer. Finally, the purchasers of the monastic estates sold their best timber to help finance and develop their acquisitions. All this was possible because of the expanding Tudor economy: new houses, shipbuilders (both naval and merchantmen), iron smelting, brewers – all were needing increasing supplies of timber which was being met by reckless clear felling, or the removal of good trees leaving only the scrub. 'Big business' of a crooked nature was soon in play; several individuals made considerable fortunes. Among them was John Mynne, who, in 1542, was made Master of King's Wood Sales – that is, from the monastic estates. Lord Lisle, later Duke of Northumberland, traded heavily and with great profit in oak from these abbey lands to be described by Albion as the first wholesale timber merchant on the grand scale. The same author considers that in the last twelve years of Henry's reign more oaks were cut than in the previous half-century. In the thirty-fifth year of his reign, Henry passed legislation commanding that when woods were felled, at least twelve good trees should be left to the acre – by any standards, an insignificant number. Edward VI made attempts to prevent the felling of oaks near the sea. These efforts to control the squandering of our woodland inheritance were, however, ineffective and soon made more so by the prodigal felling rights granted in the early years of her reign by Elizabeth I. The Elizabethan economy expanded faster and faster, and though by past standards huge quantities of timber were felled, prices rose.

Towards the middle of Elizabeth's reign there was for the first time an obvious and alarming shortage of ship timber. In 1570 Henry's act of 1543 was strengthened and Burleigh soon began to take effective action against offenders. In 1580 he ordered the sowing of acorns on thirteen acres of Windsor Park. To quote Albion again, this is 'the oldest authenticated regular plantation recorded.'

From now on until the days when the wooden ship became obsolete the Navy was continuously haunted by the fear of a famine in ship's timber. There was, therefore, an unceasing attempt by a knowledgeable minority to conserve and treat our woodlands silviculturally. This was offset by the

33. Trees and water: Brown's informality at Compton Verney, Warwickshire.

34. Trees and water: formality at Studley Royal, Yorkshire.

35. A fine Brown landscape: Harewood, Yorkshire.

36. Lombardy poplar by the River Wye, Herefordshire.

fact that so much of our timber, in the form of the Royal Forests, was still in the hands of the king. In them, he had a ready source of money. James I granted a patent to Sir Giles Mompesson – reputedly the Sir Giles Overeach in Massinger's *New Way to Pay Old Debts*, and deviser of the celebrated scheme for the licensing of innkeepers under which his and the king's pockets were well lined – for raising £100,000 a year from the royal woods.

The situation in the Weald was described romantically by Michael Drayton in his *Polyolbion* (1612):

> These forests, as I say, the daughters of the Weald,
> (*That in their heavy breasts had long their griefs concealed*)
> Foreseeing, their decay each hour so fast come on,
> Under the axe's stroke fetched many a grievous groan.
> When, as the anvil's weight, and hammer's dreadful sound,
> Even rent the hollow woods and shook the queachy ground,
> So that the trembling Nymphs, oppress'd through ghastly fear,
> Ran madding to the Downs with loose dishevell'd hair.
> The Sylvans that about the neighbouring woods did dwell
> Both in the tufty frith and in the mossy fell,
> Forsook their gloomy bowers, and wandered far abroad,
> When labouring carts they saw to hold their daily trade . . .

These 'iron times' were too much for them – all was being felled, and:

> Jove's oak, the warlike ash, vein'd elm, the softer beech,
> Short hazel, maple plain, light aspe, the bending wych
> Tough holly and smooth birch must altogether burn,
> What should the builder save, supplies the forger's turn,
> When under public good base private gain takes hold,
> And we, poor woeful woods, to ruin lastly sold.

This emphasises the fact that all kinds of timber went for fuel and charcoal: analysis of remains shows birch to be the most frequent.

Charles I's reign saw further disafforestation (the passing of royal forest land into private hands) – and such transactions as that between the king and Sir John Wintour, the entrepreneur of the iron industry in Dean. With certain restrictions he was in 1640 granted 18,000 acres on payment of £10,000 down, and £16,000 annually for six years and a subsequent annual rent. There was no stipulation to replant (Plate 27).

Just before the Civil War, it is estimated that three hundred iron works were consuming 300,000 tons of timber a year.

During the period of the Civil War and the Commonwealth the condition of our forests and woodlands deteriorated still further. The shortage of naval timber was becoming more pronounced, and good trees for immediate felling were readily marketable. When Charles II returned in 1660 the shortage of naval timber had become serious. During the supposedly enlightened period of the Commonwealth a final blow had been struck at our trees. The Government sold great areas of the forests on Royalist lands that had been sequestrated – an easy method of raising funds; alternatively, the Royalists sold their timber to pay fines. The Government entirely lacked foresight, as no steps were taken to conserve supplies for the future. The demands of the Navy were met on a hand-to-mouth basis from the royal forests, which supplied the trees free, and which soon became denuded of quality timber. To quote Albion once more, 'When Richard Cromwell abdicated . . . our splendid heritage of oak had been wasted. Since the days in which his namesake Thomas had been in power and destroyed the monasteries little more than a century before, the supply of timber had declined from abundance to scarcity.'

In August, 1662, the Royal Society was founded. Among its original members was John Evelyn (1620–1706). This in some ways strange personality unselfishly devoted his more extrovert activities to the Society and the pursuit of learning. After attaching himself to the Royalist cause, he discreetly left England in 1641, and travelled on the Continent. There he met fellow virtuosi of the arts and sciences, visiting a multitude of places and seeing a multitude of sights. He made notes of everything, later to be published in his rightly famous diaries. In 1653 he returned to England, leading an unobtrusive life, as did many other returning Royalists, under the Lord Protector.

With the Restoration Evelyn began to move to the forefront among the brilliant intelligentsia of the exiled Court, who had learned so much of the new arts and sciences during their enforced stay on the Continent.

The serious shortage of timber and the lack of any planning was put before the Royal Society on 10th September, 1662, by Sir Robert Moray. As a consequence, a week later he produced a paper of inquiries from the 'Honourable Principal Officer, and Commissioners of the Navy'. This was referred to Dr Jonathan Goddard (1617–1675), Gresham Professor of Physic, and a pioneer in telescopy; Dr Christopher Merret (1614–1695), librarian at the Royal College of Physicians; John Winthrop (1606–1676), who was from 1660 to his death Governor of Connecticut, and Evelyn. Goddard and Winthrop gave in papers on 24th September, Merret on 1st October. On that date Evelyn was asked to add his observations on these papers and to make a digest of the whole. What Goddard and Merret said seems unrecorded, but Winthrop's contribution was a brief one on the possibility of building the Navy's ships in North America from local timber.

On 15th October, 1662, Evelyn recorded in his diary, 'I this day delivered my Discourse concerning Forest-trees to our Society upon the occasion of Certaine Queries sent us by the Commissioners of His Majesties Navy.'

It was the case of the hour and the man. Whatever contribution Goddard, Merret and Winthrop made can be disregarded. To anyone reading Evelyn's *Diaries*, or knowing anything of his activities, it is clear that trees and all to do with them had long been, and were to remain until his death, the most absorbing – one might say, with religion, the most passionate – of his numerous interests. We do not know the text of the original discourse, but it so impressed the Fellows that 'he was desired to print the paper read by him'. This was the first publication made by the Society and was issued as a folio volume in 1664. It is clear that Evelyn had by then collected a prodigious amount of information ranging from practical and personal observations to legendary classical allusions on matters concerning those trees which could, or might, be grown in our islands.

He gave copies to several influential persons, headed by Charles II. His Majesty was greatly impressed and thanked him personally. As a result Evelyn was brought into the royal circle.

The first edition included also *Pomona*, a study of cider making, and his *Kalendarium Hortense*, a most interesting sidelight on seventeenth-century gardening practice. The volume was at once a success.

At the end of the Society's *Philosophical Transactions*, second volume (1666), is a note inserted at the request of Evelyn stating that at the solicitation of many worthy persons he was preparing a second edition of his Discourse and would welcome any additions, such to be sent to Mr H. Oldenburgh, one of the secretaries of the Society, 'at his house in the Palmal of St Jame's Fields, Westminster, before Lady-day next'.

The first edition of over a thousand copies was sold within two years. The second edition appeared in 1670. The dedication, now to the King, claimed that his work had been 'the sole occasion of furnishing your almost exhausted Dominions with more than two Millions of Timber Trees'.

In 1679 Evelyn issued a third revised edition. He now regretted that under his arrangements with the printers the profits, which were unexpectedly large, went to them and not to the Society. There was a fourth edition, still further revised and added to by Evelyn in 1706, the year he died. This was reprinted in 1729.

This publication, with its weight of learning and accumulation of practical wisdom, remains of remarkable interest, a deep and almost unfathomable mine of arboricultural knowledge.

Sylva had not, however, ended its career. Alexander Hunter, M.D. (1729–1809), a Scot, produced a new edition, heavily annotated, in 1776. The notes are of considerable interest. Further editions of this were published in 1786, 1801 and 1812, this last containing an account of Hunter's life. At these latter dates our supply of ship's timber was again as precarious as when Evelyn was working on his original discourse.

Few men can have done more to encourage the planting of trees, the preservation of our woodlands and the study of both than Evelyn.

Alas, except for the action of that great standby of all forestry in these islands when things are bad, the enlightened body of private owners, little was done. In 1668 Parliament passed an Act to preserve and improve the Forest of Dean – the first action undertaken since that of Burleigh in 1580 – and in 1698 a similar Act for the New Forest. They were not enforced. The next century was once again a period of ineffective management.

NEW ARRIVALS

The first decades of the seventeenth century saw the introduction of three trees that are now such an integral part of our landscape that it is difficult to believe that they are foreigners of comparatively recent arrival. One, the European larch, in 1949 ranked fifth in the order of area of trees grown in England, Wales and Scotland and is the only foreign tree to have been cultivated here for so long that it has (according to some authorities) produced a sufficient number of generations for natural selection to have developed a strain best suited to our conditions. The other, the horse-chestnut, is a tree without practical use, yet there can be no part of our islands where it is not known and admired for its flowers and fruits, or conkers.

No precise date can be given for the introduction of the European larch

(*Larix decidua* or *europaea*), a tree of wide variation in its behaviour consequent upon its numerous situations in northern and central Europe (Plate 28). The qualities of the timber have been known here from early times: it has been found in Roman remains. Turner, in his *Names of Herbes* of 1548, wrote, 'Larix or larex groweth in the highest tops of the Alpes, higher than the firres do . . . it may be called in englishe a larche tree.' Gerard does not include it in his *Catalogus* (1596) of the trees, shrubs and plants that he grew. He mentions it, however, in his *Herball* of 1597, but with no indication that he knew the tree. Parkinson, in his *Paradisi* of 1629, gives us a clear description of the tree whose 'blossoms are very beautiful and delectable, being of an excellent fine crimson colour, which standing among the greene leaves, allure the eyes of the beholders to regard it with the more desire' (the first version of Tennyson's 'when rosy plumelets tuft the larch'!). He states that in England it is rare, 'noursed up with but a few, and those onely lovers of rarities', and adds that, so far as he could hear, it had not yet produced cones in this country. As cones may be produced at ten years old, and good seed crops at twenty-five, it cannot have been here for long when Parkinson wrote. It is surprising that John Ray in his *Historia Plantarum*, 1686, makes no reference to the tree, though Evelyn in *Sylva* of 1664 had described it. Clearly, it was a rarity. It was apparently being planted in Scotland in 1656 by the Brodie of Brodie near Nairn; he called it 'lorch' (Evelyn has it as 'larsh'). As late as 1791 Gilpin wrote, 'the larch we have in England, compared with the larch of the alps, is a diminutive plant. It is little more than the puny inhabitant of a garden; or the embellishment of some trifling artificial scene.' (It now has exceeded 140 feet and a girth of eighteen feet.)

A number of plantings are recorded in England between about 1712 and 1725, from which, it seems, a good number of seedlings were raised. Around 1738 some trees, including the famous Dunkeld and Blair Atholl larches, were planted in Scotland, which were to have considerable significance on the subsequent history of the tree. Many varying accounts of these and other Scottish trees have been given, the true story having been elucidated in 1963 by A. F. Mitchell. The planting of millions of larches by the Dukes of Atholl comes later in this history, with the consequence that from a tree which was little more than a novelty the larch became, as it still is, a major feature of the Scottish landscape and an important tree in most other parts of our islands. That state may, however, possibly not be much longer maintained, as, rather like the oak, it is choosy of the sites on which it will give of its best, and there are those who claim that other trees give a better return on such ground. The timber has a number of uses, particularly when circumstances cause it to be alternately wet and dry. The thinnings are widely used for fences and 'rustic' garden work. From Roman times it was used as a writing tablet and later by Italian artists on which to paint their pictures.

Of recent years, as will be described later, it has been to some extent supplanted by the Japanese larch and a cross with that species which arose at Dunkeld.

In forests, the light and airy growth, with a spire-like crown, silvery-brown wood, and the twigs thickly covered with small cones, make it a beautiful sight in winter. Spring has few fresher greens than the breaking leaves. Unlike Tennyson, Wordsworth, a poet of little elegance in taste, set a fashion of disliking the tree.

Of the other early seventeenth-century introductions the horse-chestnut, an economically useless tree, one whose form Gilpin described as heavy and disagreeable and other writers as a tree of suburban vulgarity, is, in fact, when well grown a tree of great and rather strange magnificence, intensely admired and planted by those arbiters of taste, the French, in the glorious formal gardens of the age of Louis XIV, and painted by such artists as Puvis de Chavannes, Tissot, and our own Pre-Raphaelites.

Few trees are more popular. In the last days of winter, branches of the 'sticky buds' are torn off in a wholesale manner for the pleasure of watching the opening of the soft, woolly young leaves, to give a premature hint of spring in thousands of town dwellings. In May the flowers – no native tree can compete with them for size and grandeur – decorate town and country equally with their candles. Then, in autumn, brickbats fly, to knock down the valued 'conkers'. Finally, the gold and crimson of falling leaves light up autumn.

Few trees are now so typical of the British Isles. Yet Shakespeare does not mention it, nor even the nineteenth-century John Clare, that microscope-eyed poet of the Northamptonshire scene, who so delighted in childish games.

The reason is simple. The tree was not brought to England until about the time of Shakespeare's death, and may well not yet have been common in the remote country district where Clare spent his childhood. In 1664, Evelyn described it as a rarity and urged his readers to plant it, assuring them that it was hardy in our 'cold country'.

The first record we have of a tree growing in England is at John Tradescant's Lambeth garden in 1633. The first two trees believed to have been planted in Scotland, at Dawyck, in about 1650, survived till they were wrecked by a gale in 1912.

It was almost certainly introduced here from France. It was unknown to European botanists until described by the Italian Pierandria Mattioli, who in 1557 received specimens from Ogier Busbeq, a Flemish traveller in Turkey, that country of flower lovers, where it was grown. Mattioli gave it the name *Castanea equina*, because, he was told, the Turks called it *At-Kastane*, the horse-chestnut, as the nuts provided a remedy for horses suffering from broken wind or coughs. It was first grown in Europe at Vienna, by Charles de L'Ecluse, who raised it from seed. In 1601, in his *Rariorum Plantarum Historiae*, he published a fine engraving of it, with the French name *Chastagne de Cheval* and the Italian *Castagna de Cavalla*. In 1615, a certain Bachelier, who is only remembered for having a garden of rare plants, brought nuts to Paris from Constantinople. Cardinal Richelieu was probably the first to plant them extensively around his house at Rueil. They were planted in great numbers at Versailles and elsewhere from about the middle of the seventeenth century as one of the principal trees used in the formal gardens of Le Nôtre. In the reigns of William and Mary and Anne, London and Wise used them in a similar fashion. The name is now *Aesculus hippocastanum*.

The tree was always believed to have come to Turkey from India. A French dictionary still calls it *marronier d'Inde*, though in fact the epithet is now generally dropped. Not until 1879 was it found that it was in reality a remnant of the Tertiary Age lingering on unhappily in remote parts of the Balkans. (India has but one horse-chestnut, *Aesculus indica*, a very beautiful tree flowering some weeks later than the common kind, and sometimes seen in gardens.)

Some etymologists claim that the prefix 'horse' is no more than an indication, as in horse-radish and horse-mushroom, that this tree is an inferior form of the sweet-chestnut. They cannot have studied the early history of the tree. Nor can they be aware of the old 'doctrine of signatures' which claimed that some feature of a plant would indicate its medicinal use. The scar of the fallen leaf on the horse-chestnut is an accurate image of a horseshoe.

The name of the game 'conkers' has an origin going back far beyond the introduction of the tree and, we are told, is not a corruption of conquer. It is a development of an ancient game concerned with the crushing of snail shells, whose name has its origin in *concha*, the Latin for a mussel. In some of the midland counties, conker is replaced by cobbler. This again is a corruption of *cobillers*, a game played with nuts long pre-horse-chestnut, and of the same origin as cob-nut.

This is an appropriate stage to mention the common or Norway spruce (*Picea abies* or *excelsa*) (Plate 30). There is some doubt concerning the date of its introduction. Some authorities would have it much earlier than this, though the facts will probably never be ascertained owing to the long established use of the name 'fir' both for this tree and the Scots pine. However, Parkinson in 1629 gives a full account of it and an accurate illustration, adding that 'the use of this tree is grown with us of late days to be more frequent for the building of houses'. But this is more likely to refer to the imported timber, commonly known as deal, than to trees grown in this country. The Norway spruce has a wide range in Europe and is therefore tolerant of a wide range of conditions in our islands. It was present here in pre-glacial times, but never returned.

It is also difficult, from the confusion of names already mentioned, to trace its use as a forest tree. By the late eighteenth century, however, it was evidently quite common and was described in some detail by the Rev. William Gilpin.

Subsequently, and particularly during the present century, it has been widely planted because of its good timber qualities and its adaptability to varying sites. In recent years it has been raised in large numbers to provide Christmas trees. It is traditionally used also as a nurse crop – that is, to provide physical protection for slower growing trees, such as oak, and to supply saleable timber before the final crop is ready for felling.

The Norway spruce was the principal conifer planted in the early large-scale afforestation schemes such as that around Lake Vyrnwy. A little later it was an almost ubiquitous element in Forestry Commission plantings. It is probably the tree that was responsible for such phrases as 'regimented rows of sombre conifers'. It is therefore amusing to learn that Gilpin, as a matter of taste, in an age of good taste, considered it superior to our native Scots pine.

Parkinson also makes one of the earliest references to the presence of the evergreen holm oak or ilex (*Quercus ilex*) from the Mediterranean region. Though this is not a feature of most of our landscape except as a park tree, its ability to stand sea winds has caused it to be planted in considerable numbers in some seaside localities, such as Norfolk and Suffolk, as well as in the south and west. It is, for example, a major tree in the plantings made by the Prince Consort on the Isle of Wight.

It is only assumption to state that the common lime (*Tilia vulgaris* or *europaea*) was introduced during the early sixteenth century, but it is not improbable. First, however, it would be well to define what the epithet 'common' means, an epithet that, as was mentioned earlier, is today justified. It is again assumption that it is a hybrid between the large-leaved (*T. platyphyllos*) and small-leaved (*T. cordata*) limes, both of which are native. Though both species have grown together in this country, the evidence that the cross has occurred naturally here is not satisfactory. There is at least one good reason why it should not happen: in the same situation, the large-leaved flowers before the small-leaved, with a gap between. Exceptional climatic conditions might, of course, prove the rule wrong.

Very few references are made to lime trees in early literature. In 1612 Bacon mentions the flowering of the lime tree (in July) as one of the plants that 'doe best perfume the Aire'. In 1629, Parkinson refers to two kinds, the 'male' and the 'female', but only describes the 'female' – probably the small-leaved – which, he says, is planted to make arbours and summer banqueting houses. He does not mention a distinguishing feature of the common lime (otherwise midway between the two): that is, the remarkable bushy growths of twigs occurring on the trunk and branches (those at the base of the tree are not, as seems to be the case, suckers, but growths from the bole). Parkinson observed so closely that surely he would have mentioned this.

The earliest reference to an English lime avenue, or perhaps alley-way is a more accurate description, is on John Smythson's plan for Wimbledon House of 1609. There appear some twenty-seven trees on either side planted 'both for shade and sweetness'. Again, no indication of the kind is given.

One is forced, therefore, to draw conclusions from living lime avenues of great age, such as that at Buxted, Sussex, believed to have been planted in 1630. This is certainly *Tilia vulgaris*, as are virtually all the other lime avenues that avoided murder during the landscape vogue, and those planted subsequently.

There can be little doubt that this was the lime generally used for the age of avenues (Plate 29), following the fashion the Court had learned from Le Nôtre while on the Continent: 'We send commonly for this tree into Flanders and Holland (which indeed grow not so naturally wild with us) to our excessive cost, while our own woods do in some places spontaneously; and though of somewhat a smaller leaf, yet altogether as good . . .' This suggests that the European lime was being brought over from the Continent and that the native lime Evelyn referred to (in 1664) was the small-leaved *T. cordata*.

That this is so there can be little doubt, for there are a number of instances of trees and avenues planted at the end of the seventeenth and beginning of the eighteenth century which are all the common, European lime. The extent of the importation of young trees was considerable. In 1662, for example, Christian van Vranen was granted a pass to fetch 4,000 lime trees from Holland for Hampton Court.

With the arrival of nature and informality, the lime became unpopular, not only in avenues, but because even when free growing the form of the common lime is erect and narrow. In 1788 William Cowper wrote to Lady Hesketh telling her that the limes in the 'colonnade' at Weston had been displaced, 'because, forsooth, they are rectilinear. It is a wonder they do not quarrel with a sunbeam'. By 1795 Humphry Repton had relented a little: 'The eye of taste or experience hates compulsion and turns away in disgust from every artificial means of attracting it; for this reason an avenue is most pleasing, which, like that at Langley Park, climbs up a hill and, passing over the summit, leaves the fancy to conceive its termination.'

Certainly, a revival of planting lime avenues occurred in the nineteenth century. The great avenue at Malvern Hall, Solihull, was planted by H. G. Lewis, Constable's patron, to celebrate the victory at Waterloo. 1840 saw the planting of the longest avenue in Britain, at Clumber Park in Nottinghamshire. For three miles a double-sided line of the common lime winds on either side of a main drive.

It is sad that the astute Dutch discovered how quickly – and profitably – *Tilia vulgaris* could be propagated from layers. This tree, with its ugly burrs and bushy patches, is in every way inferior to our two natives, both most beautiful trees.

The other tree that we owe to the seventeenth century is the principal feature of many townscapes. During the present century it has become universally known as the London plane (*Platanus hybrida* or *acerifolia*) (Plate 31). Though very variable in form, it is roughly intermediate between the oriental plane (*P. orientalis*), a native of south-east Europe and western Asia, and the 'American sycamore' or button-wood of eastern North America (*P. occidentalis*). It is not known in a wild state.

There are two opinions on its origin. First, that it is a 'sport' from the oriental plane. Second, that it is a hybrid that has mysteriously arisen between one species restricted to the orient and another found only in the New World.

All that is known for certain is that the London plane made its first appearance in about 1666 in the Oxford Botanic Garden as *Platanus inter et occidentalum media* – a plane between the oriental and western (American) plane. As perhaps the finest and almost certainly the oldest London plane is at Ely, and there are good grounds for thinking that it might well have been taken there from Oxford, it was suggested by Dr Augustine Henry that the London plane arose as a chance hybrid seedling or seedlings in the Oxford garden, where it is known that the two putative parents grew, some time about 1666.

To investigate this theory, it is interesting to consider these parents individually. The oriental plane, though not common in this country (it should be much more grown), is from time to time seen in parks and collections. Even in our northern climate it bears all the qualities that the ancients attributed to it: 'Platanus, that so beautiful and precious tree, so doated on by Xerxes, that Aelian and other authors tell us he made a halt, and stop'd his prodigious army of seventeen hundred thousand souldiers, which even cover'd the sea, exhausted rivers, and thrust Mount Athos from the Continent, to admire the pulchritude, and procerity of one of these goodly trees, and became so fond of it, that spoiling both himself, his concubines, and great persons of all their jewels, he cover'd it with gold, gemms, neck-laces, scarfs and bracelets, and infinite riches; in sum, was so enamor'd of it, that for some days, neither the concernment of his grand Expedition, nor interest of honour, nor the necessary motion of his portentous Army, could perswade him from it.' So wrote Evelyn.

This great tree was a surprisingly early arrival in England. Between 1582 and 1592 Anthony Watson, Rector of Cheam, visited the palace of Nonsuch and described 'a widespreading circular plane tree, its branches supported on posts, so that many people can sit beneath it'. That is an accurate description of an aged oriental plane.

Turning to the American plane, it was a much later arrival. The first record is of two small plants in John Tradescant's Lambeth garden in 1631. And now we come to the snag in the theory of an Oxford origin: it is very doubtful if this plane has ever lived to flowering stage in this country.

It may be, therefore, that the London plane is a sport of the oriental plane. Against this is the fact that seedlings of the London plane are variable, as if hybrids.

If we start guessing, with a little historical knowledge of plant introduction, it is not impossible that early travellers brought the American plane back to Spain, where the oriental plane had long been grown, and that the cross occurred there.

The London plane was not planted in London in large numbers until about 1811, when the major developments with which John Nash was concerned were begun. Some of the oldest London trees are those in Berkeley Square, planted in 1789.

Probably the largest example in the British Isles is the tree in the Bishop's Palace at Ely, which in 1960 was 114 feet high and just over 26 feet in girth.

The presence of that most famous of trees, the cedar of Lebanon (Plate 32), used in the construction of Solomon's temple and other famous buildings, was first mentioned in 1659 when an accurate description was made of seedlings, then scarce. It is also likely that a tree, no longer standing, at Wilton was planted in about 1638. At Childrey, near Wantage, there is a cedar still standing that may well have been planted by Dr Edward Pococke, the rector, an orientalist, in 1646. It was rare until 1732 in which year it first bore cones in England. Probably the first extensive planting was by the Duke of Richmond at Goodwood in about 1760. At that period Lancelot Brown was using it in his landscapes – almost the only exotic conifer that he selected.

This massive, tabulaeform tree is limited in the wild in both numbers and area, growing only in the mountains of Lebanon and the Cilician Taurus. The name cedar evolves from the Greek *kedros*, which was a now unidentifiable tree with resinous, fragrant wood. Hence a number of trees with these qualities have in the course of time been named cedar in the vernacular, to the annoyance of botanists, who limit the name to the small genus they have called *Cedrus*.

CHAPTER FOUR

The Landscape Devised

'I HAVE NOT SEEN any garden in Italy worth taking notice of. The Italians fall as short of the French in this particular, as they excel them in their palaces. It must, however, be said to the honour of the Italians, that the French took from them the first plans of their gardens, as well as of their waterworks; so that the surpassing of them at present is to be attributed to their riches rather than the excellence of their taste.'

So wrote Joseph Addison in his *Remarks on Several Parts of Italy in the Years 1701, 1702, 1703*. In 1699 he had written to Congreve: 'I am so singular as to prefer Fontainebleau. It is situated among rocks and woods that give you a fine variety of savage prospects.'

It is interesting to see what interested and excited Addison on his Italian journeyings. '. . . there is nothing about Naples, nor indeed in any part of Italy, which deserves our admiration so much as this mountain (Vesuvius).' Then follows a graphic dramatic account of his climb to its summit, with a surprisingly careful description of the physical details of this mountain, whose top he discovered to be 'a wide, naked plain, smoking with sulphur in several places, and probably undermined with fire'.

It is true that on the Continent mountains had long been admired, if not with enthusiasm then at least with awe. Early in the fourteenth century Petrarch, on reaching the summit of Mount Ventoux, opened his copy of the *Confessions of St Augustine* and read: 'Men go to admire the heights of mountains, the great floods of the sea, the floods of the ocean, and the orbits of the stars, and neglect themselves.' And in 1541 Conrad Gesner 'resolved for the future, so long as God grants me life, to ascend divers mountains every year. . . . What must be the pleasure, think you, what the delight of a mind rightly touched, to gaze upon the huge

93

mountain masses for one's show, and, as it were, lift one's head into the clouds? The soul is strangely rapt with these astonishing heights.'

Yet in England the idea of mountains raised nothing but horror. In 1624 the anonymous authors of *A Relation of a Short Survey of Twenty-six Counties* wrote of our own modestly mountainous Lake District that it was 'nothing but hideous hanging hills and great pooles, that in what respect of the murmuring noyse of those great waters, and those high, mountainous, tumbling, rocky hills, a man would think he were in another world'.

In about 1651 Andrew Marvell, returned from the Continent when he had viewed the Alps, wrote *Upon the Hill and Grove at Bill-borow*:

> See how the archèd Earth does here
> Rise in a perfect Hemisphere!
> The stiffest Compass could not strike
> A Line more circular and like;
> Nor softest Pensel draw a Brow
> So equal as this Hill does bow.
> It seems as for a Model laid,
> And that the World by it was made.
> Here learn ye Mountains more unjust,
> Which to abrupter greatness thrust,
> That do with your hook-shoulder'd height
> The Earth deform, and Heaven fright.
> For whose excresence, ill design'd,
> Nature must a new Centre find . . .

And a little later, 1667, there is Dryden in his *Indian Emperor*: 'High objects, it is true, attract the sight: but it looks up with pain on craggy rocks and barren mountains.'

Still closer in time to Addison's Vesuvian rhapsody was Charles Cotton's *Warden of the Peak* of 1681, when the valleys were:

> 'Environ'd round with nature's shames and ills,
> Black heath, wild rock, bleak crags and naked hills.'

Addison was looking at the landscape, too, with a new vision. 'I must confess,' he wrote, 'I was most pleased with a beautiful prospect that none of them [the itineraries] have mentioned.' It was the view 'into the Roman Campania, where the eye loses itself on a smooth spacious plain.

On the other side is a more broken and interrupted scene, made up of an infinite variety of inequalities and shadowings, that naturally arise from an agreeable mixture of hills, groves and valleys. But the most enlivening part of all is the river Teverone, which you see at about a quarter of mile's distance, throwing itself down a precipice, and falling by several cascades from one rock to another, till it gains the bottom of the valley, when the sight of it would be quite lost, did it not sometimes discover itself through the breaks and openings of the woods that grow about it. The Roman painters often work upon this landscape. . . .'

Temple had denounced as recently as 1685 with distaste the generally accepted approval of the supposedly Chinese system of irregularity in garden designs and 'sharawadgi'. At the time Addison wrote, the grandiose formal garden at Blenheim had not even been planned, Lord Cobham (as he was to become) had not embarked on his exploration of new styles at Stowe nor had Aislabie begun work at Studley Royal (Plate 34). Even Pope's great nature poem, *Windsor Forest*, did not appear until 1713. No public practical manifestation of the new emotions appeared until some years later, with one exception, which was not described until 1718 when Stephen Switzer wrote that at Castle Howard, in Wray Wood, 'where Mr London[1] designed a star, which would have spoiled the wood, but that his Lordship's superlative genius prevented it, and to the great advancement of the design, had given it that labyrinth-diverting model we now see it'. Castle Howard was begun to Vanbrugh's design in 1699. Was he, who later fought for the preservation, on what we should now call romantic grounds, of the old manor house at Woodstock at Blenheim, the real inspiration for this change?

We are surely justified in thinking that the ideas – and, one repeats, the emotions – underlying the landscape garden originated in the last years of the seventeenth century. The revolutionary elements that composed them had somehow got into Addison's head long before his famous attack on formality and praising *sharawadgi* in 1712.

It is interesting to probe further into this revolutionary change of outlook, which was eventually to influence garden design, and, indeed, a wide field of thought throughout much of the world. Temple's reference to *sharawadgi* meant no more, in fact, than a mention of irregularity, for nothing was known of the details of Chinese gardening for several decades more. The landscape movement was based on the irregular

---

[1] George London, who died in 1713, was the most prolific of the English garden designers who worked in the style of Le Nôtre.

beauties of nature and its wild moods and situations, of the association of water and trees, and particularly on the paintings of Claude, Poussin, Salvator Rosa and their school, with the overtones and echoes of ancient civilisations seen in their pictures.

The new fashion seems to have originated among the Whigs, to which party Addison belonged. They were, as a party, opposed to Louis XIV and presumably all that he and his court, including Le Nôtre, stood for. It was also the party of dissent and Dissenters. Another Whig was Anthony, Earl of Shaftesbury, whose thoughts, embodied in his *Characteristics*, must have been evolving long before its publication in 1711. In a footnote in his *Miscellaneous Reflections* is the remarkable passage on gardens:

'Behold the Disposition and Order of these finer sorts of Apartments, Gardens, *Villas*! The kind of Harmony to the Eye, from the various Shapes and Colours agreeably mixt, and rang'd in Lines, intercrossing without confusion, and fortunately co-incident. – A *Parterre*, Cypresses, Groves, Wildernesses. – Statues, here and there, of *Virtue*, *Fortitude*, *Temperance*. – *Heroe's* – Busts, *Philosopher's* Heads, with suitable Mottos and Inscriptions. Solemn Representations of things deeply natural. *Caves*, *Grottos*, *Rocks* – *Urns* and *Obelisks* in retir'd places, and dispos'd at proper distances and points of Sight: with all those Symmetrys which silently express a reigning *Order*, *Peace*, *Harmony* and *Beauty*! – But what is there answerable to this, in the MINDS of the *Possessors*? – What *Possession* or *Propriety* is theirs? What *Constancy* or *Security* of Enjoyment? What *Peace*, what *Harmony* WITHIN.'

Elsewhere he states: 'I shall no longer resist the passion growing in me for things of a natural kind; when neither art, nor the conceit or caprice of man has spoil'd their genuine order, by breaking in upon that primitive state. Even the rude rocks, the mossy caverns, the irregular unwrought grottos, and broken falls of waters, with all the horrid graces of the wilderness itself, as representing Nature more, will be the more engaging and appear with a magnificence beyond the formal mockery of princely gardens.'

Here in the new spirit of the age, the ferment that had been working among a body of men, which fired Addison with delights in the rockiness of Fontainebleau, the bleak pumice of Vesuvio, and a distaste for the most beautiful gardens in the world – which he (surely not of an inventive turn of mind) had expressed some years before this was published in 1709.

37. In the
Reptonian manner:
Tatton Park,
Cheshire.

38. A Repton
landscape:
Rudding Park,
Cheshire.

39. 'One dull, vapid, smooth and tranquil scene'— Brown, Audley End.

40. Early nineteenth-century oakwoods, now valueless; New Forest, Hampshire.

41. Douglas Fir;
Putley,
Herefordshire.

42. Monterey
Pine; Dartington
Hall, Devon.

43. Giant red-
wood; Leighton,
Montgomeryshire.

44. Welling-
tonia; Titten-
hurst, Berkshire.

The general feeling and seeking for nature swells steadily. In 1713 there was Bishop Berkeley:

'Is there not something in the woods and groves, in the rivers and clear springs, that soothes and delights, that transports the soul?'

And in the same year, the Countess of Winchilsea's *The Petition for an Absolute Retreat* begins:

> *Give me, Oh indulgent fate!*
> *Give me yet, before I die,*
> *A sweet but absolute retreat,*
> *'Mongst paths so lost, and trees so high,*
> *That the world may ne'er invade*
> *Through such windings and such shade*
> *My unshaken liberty.*

Slightly varied, '*such windings and such shade*' appear, significantly, as a refrain throughout this long and lovely poem.

In 1718 we find, in the first writer on the new principles of gardening, Stephen Switzer, using the phrase 'that inexpressible somewhat to be found in the beauty of nature'.

A whole new aesthetic attitude towards the landscape, not only to the design of gardens, had come into being – though it was at first slow in its practical adoption. Though subsequent writers were inclined to call in Spenser, Bacon and Milton as its originators (and later the French brought in the Chinese), these authors surely provided no more than a few hints and decorative ideas useful as English precedents. The underlying principle was philosophical and even psychological, with its emphasis on freedom (after the abstract, entirely restrictive art that the French had evolved from the Italian model).[1]

So far as trees were concerned, the first result was freeing them from the tyranny of the shears, and breaking the irregularity of the forms of bosquets and avenues. Within a few decades, the garden had taken in large areas of parkland as a planned landscape formed from trees (vast numbers of them) carefully placed in irregular patterns, grass, winding paths, and lakes with equally winding margins. Around this new area of taste–the conception not of gardeners and architects, but of philosophers, poets and

---

[1] It is well to recall that the philosophical works of Burke (1756) and Lord Kames (1762) were late-comers, and not originators of the new outlook.

writers – there was soon to arise, from the nature of its origins, a great body of literature.

At this stage, when nature and landscape became so much the concern of the cultured British, it is appropriate to comment on their previous entire neglect by British artists. It is generally held that the first of our painters to treat landscape as a subject in its own right was George Lambert (1710–65), trained as portraitist and scene painter. The landscapes in drawings or paintings by our earlier artists were merely inconsequential topographical backgrounds, usually of mansions. Therefore, it is of singular interest to walk round our galleries to observe how profoundly landscape had previously been studied by continental artists, not only as a background, but as an end in itself. In the British Museum is Dürer's remarkably atmospheric water- and body-colour sketch described as 'a lake bordered by pine trees' (though they are surely spruces) – a pure, inhuman landscape. The artist died in 1538. And there is the exquisite sketch of a slender tree clinging to a bank by the Italian Frederico Barocci (1526–1612).

In the National Gallery is the strange, careful oil painting of a building, a footbridge, and trees – the trees having great significance – painted by Albrecht Altdorfer between 1518 and 1520.[1] In the same institution may be seen two of the most magnificent landscapes ever painted, those by Rubens (1577–1640). The *Château de Steen* is a distant landscape that rolls over the countryside till it joins with the sky, with the château closer at hand, the gateway and the tops of the tree adjoining it caught in a gleam of sun. A wagon rumbles along and a fowler stalks birds, oblivious of the wide scene of land and air behind them and a charm of goldfinches unconcernedly flits in the bushes. *Landscape: Sunset*, another great canvas, has even less of humanity in it – no more than a shepherd, his dog and sheep, with some distant buildings, which are not noticed until the eye has looked over the oaks and silver birches and the water to a primrose evening sky.

So far as date is concerned, Rembrandt (1608–69) and Ruysdael (1628–82), two others who entirely grasped the significance of the natural scene, are more or less contemporaneous with the painters who provided the inspiration (and formulae) for the landscape garden: most were later quaintly named in rather incongruous association by William Hutchinson in 1776:

[1] The same artist's equally astonishing painting of a tiny, mounted St George, who prances at the dragon, is in reality a complex, realistic woodland landscape. It is reproduced in Sir Kenneth Clark's *Landscape Into Art*.

'The painting of Poussin describe the nobleness of Uls-water; the works of Salvator Rosa express the romantic and rocky scene of Keswick, and the tender elegant touch of Claude Lorraine, and Smith, pencil forth the rich variety of Windermere.'

George Smith (1713–76) is not, to say the least, usually bracketed with Lorraine, and Hutchinson omits Francesco Albani, who is usually one of those included. All these men worked in the middle decades of the seventeenth century; the oldest of them, Nicolas Poussin, born in 1594, did not take to landscape until about 1648. Gaspard Poussin, the protégé of Nicholas and a younger man, is also usually included among these masters.

To describe their work is beyond our purpose; examples of it may be seen in many collections. Appreciation of its value has, of course, varied with changing fashions.[1] Not only were they seen on the grand tours of the eighteenth century, but they were discussed in the writings of Jonathan Richardson (1665-1749). They all have an air of unreality, of being part of the classical myths and legends which are so often their nominal subjects, and quite devoid of the earthiness found in Altdorfer, Dürer and Rubens. They were elysiums, arcadias, paradises – in short, not of this world.

From these mixed origins arose the landscape garden. The story, in Horace Walpole's words, is now well enough known. It is obviously incomplete, for the only names mentioned are Charles Bridgeman and William Kent. Bridgeman, Walpole suspected, evolved 'the capital stroke . . . the destruction of walls for boundaries, and the invention of fossés – an attempt then deemed so astonishing that the common people called them Ha! Ha's! to express their surprise at finding a sudden and unperceived check to their walk'.

The ha-ha was described, and this explanation of the name given, in A. J. D. d'Argenville's *La Théorie et la Pratique du Jardinage*, of 1709 – a treatise on formal gardening, translated into English by John James in 1712. There is evidence that Walpole's claim is correct, for in his *Tour Through England and Wales* of 1724 Defoe wrote of Blenheim that the pleasure garden was 'a very large plot of ground taken out of the park . . . it may still be said to be a part of it, well contriv'd by sinking the outer wall into a foss, to give a view quite round, and take off the odious appearance of confinement and limitation to the eye. It is well adorned with walls, greens, espaliers, and vistas to divers remarkable objects that offer themselves in

[1] A recent and carefully considered view will be found in Sir Kenneth Clark's *Landscape Into Art*.

the circumjacent country.' The garden at Blenheim was the work of the formalist Henry Wise, but Bridgeman worked there between 1709 and 1730, as did Stephen Switzer, the first *practical* gardener to write on the new style.

The other name mentioned by Walpole was Kent, who at that moment fortuitously appeared, 'painter enough to taste the charms of landscape, bold and opinionative enough to dare and dictate, and born with a genius to strike out a great system from the twilight of imperfect essays. He leaped the fence, and saw that all nature was a garden.'

William Kent (1684–1748), protégé of the third Earl of Burlington (1694–1753), was brought back from Italy in 1719, and with his master, who set about Palladianising our architecture, also set about revolutionising our gardens.

Of this there is no doubt. An example of the new style, apparently the progenitor of the popular *ferme ornée* (in spite of the name, entirely English), was Philip Southcote's Wooburn (or Woburn) Farm near Chertsey. On a larger scale, we have Kent's Rousham in the Cherwell valley, of about 1738, still corresponding with more or less contemporary plans. The violent wrench of the departure from former practice of this design, on steep unterraced banks conforming to two right-angled bends in the river, is astounding.

However, our concern is with the use of trees – Rousham is richly wooded – and here we may return to Walpole again. Kent, he said, worked on the great principles of 'perspective, light and shade. Groups of trees broke too uniform or too extensive a lawn; evergreens and woods were opposed to the glare of the champain, and when the view was less fortunate, or so much exposed to be beheld at once, he blotted out some parts by thick shades, to divide it into variety, or to make the richest scene more enchanting by reserving it to a farther advance of the spectator's step. Thus selecting favourite objects, and veiling deformities by screens of plantation; sometimes allowing the rudest waste to add its foil to the richest theatre, he realised the compositions of the greatest masters in painting. Where objects were wanting to animate his horizon, his taste as an architect could bestow immediate termination. . . .

'But of all the beauties he added to the face of this beautiful country, none surpassed his management of water. Adieu to canals, circular basins, and cascades tumbling down marble steps, that last absurd magnificence of Italian and French villas. . . . The gentle stream was taught to serpentise seemingly at its pleasure, and when discontinued by different levels, its course appeared to be concealed by thickets properly inter-spersed, and glittered again at a distance where it might be supposed naturally to arrive. . . .

'A few trees scattered here and there on its edges sprinkled the tame bank that accompanied its maeanders; and when it disappeared among the hills, shades descending from the heights leaned towards its progress, and framed the distant point of light under which it was lost, as it turned aside to either hand of the blue horizon.'

Thus were described in an idealised manner the fundamentals of the English landscape garden which, after numerous vicissitudes of taste in its manner of achievement, was in the course of time to alter much of the British open landscape, and to spread its inspiration over the world.

During the eighteenth century and after, it led to much planting of trees, largely, but by no means entirely, for effect. Our usual timber trees predominated, and from time to time, particularly during wars, yielded valuable crops to the descendants of their planters.

It is important, however, to realise that some of the earliest examples of the English landscape garden were unlike the very numerous eighteenth-century survivors – mostly designed by Brown, Repton and their followers, where native trees predominate, as they did, so far as Kent's sketches and surviving gardens suggest, in those he designed.

Southcote's pioneering *ferme ornée* begun in 1735 contained, a century after, according to Loudon, 'one of the largest liquidambar trees in England, a remarkably fine hemlock spruce, very large tulip trees, acacias, hickories, pines, cedars, and cypresses, and a magnificent cut-leaved alder'. The Hon. Charles Hamilton laid out Painshill in Surrey a year or two later, described by the connoisseur Thomas Whately as a 'new creation; and a boldness, and a happiness of execution, attend the wonderful efforts which art has there made to rival nature'. When Loudon visited the place, among the trees remaining were 'some remarkably fine silver cedars, pinasters, and other pines, American oaks, cork trees and ilices, a tupelo tree, tulip trees, acacias, deciduous cypress, Lombardy, and other poplars . . . here some of the first rhododendrons and azaleas[1] introduced into England were planted by Mr Thoburn, who was gardener to Mr Hamilton'. Hamilton also advised Lord Shelburne (later Marquess of Lansdowne) at Bowood, which was planted with 'every kind of foreign tree that could be procured at that time'.[2]

[1] Probably North American species.
[2] This differentiation is unfortunately not now properly appreciated. This has led to

All this rich, imaginative and speculative (for some of the trees used were virtually unknown) planting was quite distinct from the methods employed by William Shenstone (1714–63) and Lancelot Brown (1716–83). Both, perhaps from force of circumstances, used a limited range of material; principally our native forest trees.

Shenstone's work must be described first not only on the slender grounds of his seniority, but because his influence was greater, particularly on the Continent, than that of Brown and his whole attitude to producing an individual, Arcadian 'landskip' was quite distinct from that of Brown, who produced design after design for his great landlord clients.

At Oxford Shenstone moved into a literary circle of some quality. He was very English, and almost insular in his disapproval of the Grand Tour. Sensitive, scholarly, the heir to a small estate near Halesowen in Worcestershire, with the land rising up steeply behind his house, so that from its heights the romantic hills of the Welsh border country could be seen, he spent a lifetime aiming at perfection in miniature.

Shenstone was friendly with the Graves family of Mickleton,[1] whom he used to visit, and the account of his contemporary Richard Graves is the best description of the origins of the Leasowes:

'At Mickleton, Mr Shenstone seems to have conceived the first idea of attempting what proved the most fortunate (though deemed, perhaps, by *prudent* people, the most unfortunate) undertaking in which he was ever engaged; an undertaking, at least, which made him so generally known and admired in the world, though it must be confessed, it contributed nothing to the advancement of his fortune; I mean the laying out in the modern taste and embellishing his farm at the Leasowes.

'Mr Graves[2] had been adopted as his principal heir, by a distant relation, a Mr Morgan of Warlies,[3] in Essex; who, from hints which he had borrowed from Mr Southcote's and other places, which began then to be modelled somewhat in the present style, had given Warlies under the natural disadvantages of wood and water, by removing or concealing the fences, and shewing to advantage the few groups of trees, and every distant object in the most striking light; by these contrivances, he had given his place a park-like appearance, and made it an elegant villa.

---

uninformed criticism of recent planting of 'flowering' trees and rhododendrons at Stourhead, where the tradition of over two centuries justifies the use of new exotics.

[1] Near Stratford on Avon on the land that rises up to Hidcote.

[2] Richard Graves the elder (1677–1729), antiquary.

[3] Only a rotunda remains from this period.

'This had encouraged Mr Graves to do something in the same way at Mickleton; which, though in an indifferent country, has many natural beauties; of surrounding hills, and hanging woods; a spacious lawn, and one natural cascade; capable of great improvement, though from various circumstances, the place is to this day in a very unfinished state. This, however, was sufficient to engage the attention and excite the active imagination of Mr Shenstone.

'Something of the same kind, indeed, had already been begun at Hagley also, in his own neighbourhood, but on so large a scale, and in so magnificent a style as not to raise the least idea of imitation.

'He had already, on his first coming to board with his tenant at the Leasowes, cut a straight walk through his wood, terminated by a small building of rough stone; and in a sort of gravel or marle pit, in the corner of a field, amongst some hazels, he had scooped out a sort of cave, stuck a little cross of wood over the door and called it an hermitage; and, a few years after, had built an elegant little summer house in the water, under the fine group of beeches (which was afterwards removed by Mr Pitt's advice). But hitherto Mr Shenstone had no conception of an *whole*, or of disposing his environs on any consistent plan, and giving it its present beautiful and picturesque appearance. . . .

'As the Lyttelton family, with their connections the Grenvilles and the Pitts,[1] were all people of taste, and had been much at Stowe, they were very intent upon embellishing Hagley Park; and as they were, during the recess, in the country, they frequently went over to the Leasowes, after Mr Shenstone had brought it into some degree of perfection.

'Mr William Pitt (afterwards Lord Chatham) was particularly charmed with the place; and once observed to Mr Shenstone, that *Nature had done everything for him*; to which Mr Shenstone replied that *he hoped he had done something for Nature too*, by displaying her beauties to the best advantage. Mr William Pitt, afterwards though a younger brother, and his fortune then not large – with a noble contempt of money, any further than as a means of doing good, or conferring favours – as he saw several possible improvements which Mr Shenstone could not execute, gave him an hint, by means of Mr Miller of Radway, that, with his permission, Mr Pitt would please himself by laying out two hundred pounds at the Leasowes. This, however, Mr Shenstone considered as a species of dalliance with his *mistress*, to which he could not submit . . . having taken his farm at the Leasowes into his own hands, about the year 1745, as Dr Johnson says,

---

[1] Note the political connections, also.

began now to extend his plan, and to form it into one connected whole, by a line of walk, to shew its several beauties in the most striking light, and to give it a picturesque appearance on the principles of landscape gardening, which he told me he had reduced to a regular system.

'The idea, "that a landscape-painter would be the best English gardener", Mr Shenstone, I believe, first expressed and pursued in his "Thoughts on Gardening" though Kent, and other designers of this century, must have had an idea of the thing intended. This subject the amiable and very ingenious Monsieur Girardin Viscount d'Ermenonville has since developed in his elegant and useful treatise "on the Means of improving the Country round our Habitations". It must be confessed, however, that he has greatly improved on Mr Shenstone's system in one respect, by so intimately uniting utility with rural embellishment. "A virtuous citizen," says he, "who begins with admiring picturesque landscape, which pleases the eye, will soon endeavour to produce that moral landscape which pleases the mind, by shewing the country happy around him. Nothing is more affecting than the sight of universal content." Then, after a few remarks on the beauty of a well-cultivated farm, he concludes his essay with this sensible but sarcastic reflection on the manners of the present age: "Perhaps, when every folly is exhausted, there will come a time in which men will be so far enlightened, as to prefer the real pleasures of nature to variety and chimera."

'The Marquis seems also to have availed himself of Mr Shenstone's hint, in his beautiful Villa of Ermenonville, that "wherever a park or garden happens to have been the scene of any event in history, one would surely avail one's self of that circumstance, to make it more interesting to the imagination: mottoes should allude to it; columns record it . . ."

'As Mr Shenstone, after he came to settle at the Leasowes made it his constant residence as long as he lived, he was of course continually adding to the improvements and decorations of his farm.

'He built the ruinated priory, adorned with the arms of his friends on gothic shields; he cut vistas to show, from several points of view, the beautiful spire of Hales-own; he erected urns, or placed up inscriptions, to his friends or to his favourite writers; he placed a cast of the Medicean Venus in his shrubbery; and one of the piping fawn in a small circle of firs, hazels and other elegant shrubs, which were some of the most expensive ornaments of his place; for many of his seats and cascades were made by the manual labour of an old servant, under his own direction.'

Few individuals can have affected and impressed their style upon

British parkland – and hence, even to this day, upon the landscape – than 'Capability' Brown (1716–83). With him must be included his assistants, pupils and imitators – such men as John Spyers, Lapidge, Richard Woods, and particularly William Eames, who had in turn a pupil named Sandys, and who seems to have worked also with a mysterious Mr Webb, a man with a considerable practice, particularly in the north-western counties. Finally Humphry Repton literally carried on where Brown left off, until forced by a change in fashion to alter his manner somewhat. Brown's history and work, like his nickname, were admirable. Born at Kirkharle in Northumberland of apparently humble parents, with a sound local education, he entered the gardens of Sir William Wallington, where he stayed for seven years. He was therefore, unlike many of those who transformed the English garden, a trained practical gardener. In 1739 he went south, and was employed at Wotton, not far from Aylesbury – and Stowe. His employer was Sir Richard Grenville, father-in-law of William Pitt and brother-in-law of Lord Cobham, of Stowe. These family and political connections again appear and show that the great Whig families were enthusiasts for modern gardening, which was of consequence to his future career. Within a year he entered the Stowe gardens – in the kitchen-garden, but was soon head-gardener, and working with William Kent. A year or two later he was being lent to 'improve' the grounds of Cobham's friends. By 1751 he had qualified for the approval of Horace Walpole. The grounds of Warwick Castle, he wrote, were 'well laid out by one Brown, who has set up on a few ideas of Kent and Mr Southcote'.

This work had been done while at Stowe, but in 1751 he set up as a professional landscaper at Hammersmith.

Of his remarkable career and works Miss Stroud has written authoritatively.[1] Our only purpose now is to attempt an assessment, particularly as it concerns trees, of his landscaping.

First, in terms of line, the serpentine dominated.

Second, in terms of grouping, or dotting, irregularity was the key-word.

Of surface, he worked in terms of gentle undulation again and again set around the flatness of calm sheets of water. Indeed, it can be said without hesitation now that his trees are senile that Brown's influence on our landscape remains in our innumerable ornamental lakes and pools, looking so natural and yet so artfully and skilfully conceived, in which he set a mode followed by many subsequent practitioners in design. They range from the great lake at Blenheim, whose main body of water stretches over a mile

[1] *Capability Brown*. Country Life.

and a half, to numerous examples of, say, some three hundred yards. As at Blenheim, these great waters are as often as not contrived out of some insignificant stream. Brown's handling of this new 'natural' form of hydraulics is often as touched with genius as were the canals and water-works of the formalists (Plate 33). And in their handling the often partly wooded banks, or strategically arranged clumps of trees, from behind which – actually just round the corner – the water arrives as if from afar distance, are fundamental to the illusion of the 'natural' scene (Plate 35).

His winding ribbons of trees surrounding the park to give privacy, which at the same time obscure or lose its actual limits, are sometimes less successful. His scattered clumps and isolated trees are usually excellently managed, often arranged to carry the eye and mind into the distance. Today, many an oak or group of Scots pines he planted, now aged and storm-beaten, give a sense of drama that is usually absent from his work. The greatest criticism that can be directed was, in Walpole's phrase, 'he will be least remembered; so closely did he copy nature that his works will be mistaken'. Brown's 'nature', however, has quite overlooked the wild-ness and grandeur of his Northumbrian childhood. It is suave, calm and prosperous, and designed so that – by means of the ha-ha – it comes almost up to, and is to be viewed principally from, the rooms of the house.

It is not surprising that several of his landscapes survive because they make excellent golf-courses.

Brown was a great destroyer, as were his successors. Lime and elm avenues were, with very few exceptions (such as Charlecote), eliminated. Further, because of their association with formal gardens, they were discriminated against. He used our native or long-established introduced trees, with the addition of the Lebanon cedar. Was this because of the insistence of his clients, or because of economic necessity? Growing at Claremont, one of Brown's masterpieces, there were, according to Loudon, 'a great many exotic trees' that he had planted. At his huge undertaking at Croome, for Lord Coventry, where, during the 1750s, he reclaimed (at a reputed cost of £400,000) a marshy piece of land between the Severn and Avon (and into the bargain designed a new mansion), there was by 1823 a celebrated collection of exotic trees, but perhaps these were planted subsequent to Brown's activities.

The most extreme criticism of Brown's work made by a contemporary was that of his – on occasion – unsuccessful and jealous rival Sir William Chambers, who wrote of it as resembling 'a large green field, scattered over with a few straggling trees . . . (where) he finds a little serpentine path, twining in regular S's along which he meanders, roasted by the sun, so that he resolves to see no more, but vain resolution! there is but one path; he must either drag on to the end, or return back by the tedious way he came'.

More reasoned and therefore perhaps unkinder criticism was to be made after his death – which was to fall on the shoulders of his successor, Humphry Repton.

Brown died suddenly. He had added more superb trees to our landscape and ornamental woodlands, as distinct from our forests, than any man before, or any man is likely to do in future.

No one, I think, has studied the economics of the landscape garden– though Rousseau hinted at them – and rarely was so vulgar a subject mentioned at the time, though Graves did write that Girardin improved on Shenstone by 'intimately uniting utility with rural embellishment'.

From what few figures are available, it is difficult to compare the cost of building a ha-ha with that of a wall. It depended on the availability of material in the locality, and on the method of construction.

' "What do you imagine it may have cost me to put the place into the condition you see?" ' asked Rousseau's Julia showing the garden at Clarens.

' "Well," said I, (after some prompting from M. Wolmar) "since you will have these large and massy bowers, these sloping tufts, these umbrageous thickets to be the growth of seven or eight years, and to be partly the work of art, I think you have been a good ecconomist if you done all within this vast for two thousand crowns." '

' "You have only guessed two thousand crowns too much," says she, "for it cost nothing." '

Against this, in May, 1721, there were employed in the parterre at James Brydges's Canons sixteen men and two women. The greenhouses employed thirteen men, and the kitchen garden six. There was probably also casual labour. The turf was mown, with scythes, two or three times a week.

The acres of parterre, were replaced, beyond the ha-ha, by pasture, where sheep would shave the verdure, saving the cost of mowing and building up into mutton: Whatley wrote of the Leasowes, 'it is literally a grazing farm lying round the house.'

Miss Stroud relates that at Fisherwick, near Lichfield, Brown was responsible for planting 100,000 trees, mostly oak, for Lord Donegall, and assured him that in due course they would be worth £100,000. His lordship was in 1779 awarded a medal for his plantations:

Here infant oaks by Donegall are sown
And form a sheltering forest of their own.
Cut from their trunks new navies shall arise
In after-times to glad Britannia's eyes.

Fisherwick is, like other of Brown's ornamental plantings, now open agricultural land. Elsewhere felling when the timber was good has taken place to raise funds for death duties or in times of war. Other landscape woods have survived over the centuries on account of their sporting value. Today, many help their impoverished owners to maintain their estates from the sporting rights that are let to the modern plutocracy. Even the serpentined lakes may today have an economic value, either as sources of water, or, if they are within reach of an urban population, for the letting of their fishing.

Even when a village had to be moved to improve the scene, housing was surely a better investment square yard by square yard than *parterres à la broderie.*

CHAPTER FIVE

The Eighteenth Century

CRISIS

AS THE EIGHTEENTH CENTURY progressed, the demands on our limited timber supplies increased. There was, from Elizabeth I's time onwards, a steady increase in the output of coal; at the end of the seventeenth century production was three million tons yearly.[1] But coal only supplied heat. It did not provide the charcoal essential for the 'charking' or 'coking' in the smelting of iron. The smelting and refining industries moved into the country where the timber was; for example the Knight family of ironmasters from Madeley in Shropshire moved to north Herefordshire where there were still virgin forests. The Quaker ironmasters are known to have made a serious attempt to conserve timber supplies by a system of coppicing on a fifteen-year rotation. Even late in the eighteenth century furnaces were erected at such remote places as Invergarry and Inveraray in the West Highlands. The Wealden iron industry was one of the first to move away from its early home, to the north and midlands, largely because of the shortage of wood fuel and remoteness from supplies of coal – what timber remained was largely consumed by the increasing demands of the hop-kilns.

Not until, in the early part of the eighteenth century, Abraham Darby at the Coalbrookdale Works in Shropshire discovered the process of making coke from coal did the iron industry begin to become independent of wood charcoal. Great damage had, in the meantime, been done to our forests.

Much of the valuable woodlands of Cheshire were consumed in fires under the boiling pans following the discovery of rock salt in that county

[1] Compared with 240 million tons in the early part of the twentieth century.

in 1671. Early eighteenth-century Liverpool 'rose on rock salt'. Not until towards the end of the century did coal replace wood as fuel.

And so one could continue with examples of the consumption of our remaining native woodland. In many areas into which the industrialists moved, the destruction was irrevocable and centuries would have to elapse before fine timber would grow again. In the Weald, however, a traditional system of coppicing was followed and the harm done was in due course repaired.

It is not surprising that as the eighteenth century progressed, the shortage of suitable timber for our naval craft became serious. It is well to recall that the British fleet during that century was engaged in the war with Spain (1739–48), the Seven Years War (1756–63) and the American war (1775–83).

A ship of the line was larger than most country houses. No substitution of brick or stone was possible and the rigours of the sea ruled out many kinds of wood. Even so, the structure of the 'seventy-four', whose role in Britain's sea-power was vital, involved the importation of supplies from several parts of the world. The mainmast came from Maine (supplies were cut off during the American war), the topmast from the Ukraine, the spars from Norway, and the planking floated down the Vistula to Danzig. It was the framing that came from tough, angular, open grown English oaks, which provided the 'great' and 'compass' timber – top-piece, floor piece, cathead, futtock, ordinary knee, wing knee, transom knee, crutch, stern post – and no doubt other equally interestingly named parts. Young trees were bent and bound or pinned to grow into suitable shapes.

It was the shortage of these vital pieces that limited the construction of replacements to the Navy – a ship lasted about sixty years. The oaks used were those that had passed the normal economic age for felling, which was then not beyond 120 years, and fifteen to eighteen inches in diameter. As after that, the timber was just as likely to decay and become unsound as to reach the extra value of ship's timber, the private landowner was not disposed to take the risk. There was, too, the increasing strength of our merchant navy, whose smaller ships did not need the great timbers that the Navy wanted, and which again resulted in the safer and surer, and more profitable, felling of trees before they had reached naval size.

There were other demands on large oak. The spreading canal system was to open up new areas of oakwood, but in return itself needed a large share of the timber for construction and maintenance of locks. Massive oak was needed for the dockyards required for our increased shipping. Large oak was needed for barrel staves[1] – and at the other extreme, for fortifications.

Even so, as late as 1724 the itinerant Defoe saw no cause for alarm. He wrote in his *Tour Through England and Wales* that in Sussex there were 'the great foundaries, or iron-works carried on at such a prodigious expense of wood, that even in a country almost all over-run with timber, they begin to complain of the consuming it for those furnaces, and leaving the next age to want timber for building their navies: I must own, however, that I found that complaint perfectly groundless, the three counties of Kent, Sussex and Hampshire, (all of which be contiguous to one another) being one inexhaustible store-house of timber never to be destroyed, but by a general conflagration, and able at this time to supply timber to rebuild all the royal navies in Europe'.

That there was still some massive shipbuilding timber available he shows by his account of moving trees to the builder's yard. The largest trees were getting farther and farther away from water transport for the reason that they had stood longer. Near Lewes, he saw trees that could only be moved overland in dry summers, when two-and-twenty oxen were needed to pull the 'tugs' on which they were drawn. They went to Maidstone and then by water to Chatham. If there were wet summers, the journey might take two or three years. On reaching Berkshire, he tells how the best timber from that 'very well-wooded county' was hauled to Reading, then borne down the Thames to London for building merchant ships.

The first steps on a national scale to combat this shortage seem to have been taken by Henry Baker (1698–1774). This remarkable man was poet, naturalist, and authority on the deaf-and-dumb, for whom he invented a system of teaching which provided him with a fortune. He was also Daniel Defoe's son-in-law. He took a part in founding the Royal Society of Arts in 1754. In March, 1754, he presented to that body a pamphlet written by Edward Wade – about whom little is known, 'to promote the planting of timber trees in the commons and waste ground all over the kingdom, for the supply of the navy, the employment and advantage of the poor, as well as the ornamenting of the nation'. Oak was to be given the first encouragement.

As a result, in 1757 prizes were offered by the Society to encourage the planting of oak, chestnut and elm. In 1758 Scots pine was added, and in

[1] Ireland exported large quantities.

1773 larch. A gold medal was awarded to the planter of the greatest area, a silver to the next best. These prizes continued until 1835.

The first medal was given to the Duke of Beaufort in 1758 for sowing 23 acres of oak at Hawkesbury in Gloucestershire. Scots pines received their first award in 1760, chestnut and elms in 1762. The Society later offered special premiums for the planting of larch, and a prize for an essay on its utilisation. Over the years, other prizes were awarded for essays on the techniques of planting, the suitability of species to exposed sites, and kindred subjects. Useful data were collected. Much of the information was published in the *Transactions* of the Society.

At a low estimate the competitions during their existence resulted in the planting of 50,000,000 trees, of which 20,000,000 were pines and larches, and 15,000,000 oaks.

The Society's activities during the eighteenth century alleviated, but did not make a great impression on the shortage. Still less did they have any effect on planting or management in the greatest remaining woodland under one owner – that of the Crown. On the 25th January, 1787, was presented the first of the Reports of the 'Commissioners . . . into the state and condition of the woods, forests and land revenue of the Crown'. The seventeenth, dealing with the 'present and future management of Crown lands, woods and forests', was dated 28th March, 1793.

These masterly reports of the Commissioners owe a great deal to their principal, Admiral Sir Charles Middleton, a man of great vision, energy and capability. They disclosed a long history of corruption, lack of policy, and interference for financial benefit by the Crown, and incompetence in the management of their valuable possessions, not only within recent decades, but over the centuries – for the Commission dug very deeply into past history.

The lamentable state of affairs was shown when the Commission made application to John Pitt, the then Surveyor-General of the Woods and Forests, for descriptions, plans and surveys. The result was 'that not having received from any of his predecessors any maps, surveys or other accounts of his Majesty's Woods and Forests, except a few old surveys of woods and coppices which had formerly been enclosed, he could not give us any official information'. He had, however, bought privately a number of manuscripts and books relating to the subject, which were lent to the Commissioners.

The enormity of this state of affairs is suggested by the names of the woods for which the Surveyor was responsible; their area was vast.

45. Monkey-puzzle; Dropmore, Buckinghamshire.

46. Thuja; Queenswood, Herefordshire.

47. The transformed countryside; Victorian conifers mingled with native trees, Montgomeryshire.

48. The lime avenue; Clumber Park, Nottinghamshire.

They were, in Hampshire, the New Forest, Alice Holt and Wolmer Forest and Bere Forest; in Berkshire, Windsor Forest and Cranborne Chase, Windsor Great Park, Windsor Little Park; in Surrey, Richmond Park; in Middlesex, St James's Park, Hyde Park, Bushy Park, Hampton Court Park; in Gloucestershire, Dean Forest; in Kent, Greenwich Park; in Essex, Epping Forest (formerly the ancient forest of Waltham); in Northamptonshire, Whittlewood Forest, Salcey Forest and Rockingham Forest; in Oxfordshire, Whychwood Forest; and in Nottinghamshire, Sherwood Forest.

The industry of the Commissioners was such that they produced the first comprehensive account of the history and present state of our major woodlands. Their general conclusions may well, therefore, be quoted; recapitulating though they do some matters already mentioned:

'Although our Enquiry concerning the forests has been general, yet so much do the rights of the Crown, and of individuals, vary in the different forests, and such diversity is there in the grants, fees, perquisites, claims, and reservations in them, that, to avoid confusion, we shall find it necessary to report the state of each forest separately: The underwood, the timber, the bark, the top and lop, the deer, the herbage, the mines, and the soil itself, are all the subjects of different grants or reservations; and those grants are to persons of various descriptions, to officers during pleasure, for life, or in perpetuity, and to many individuals who have estates and possessions within or adjoining to the forests.

'But it is not our intention, in this Report, to attempt to explain the situation of all the forests in these particulars, or to give an accurate statement of the produce and expenditure in each of them, we think it necessary to mention, in general, in order to show how much the subject calls for the public attention, that according to the information which we have received from very able surveyors, employed in almost every part of England, there is a general and alarming decrease in the quantity of naval timber, both in the forests, and on private estates: That there is less ground new planted than of wood land turned into tillage; and that the plantations now made are, in general, more for ornament than use: That the annual demand for the dock yards cannot, from the accounts which we have received from the Navy Board, be reckoned at less than 25,000 tons or loads, of which quantity not more than one twelfth part has been furnished from the whole of the forests of the Crown during His Majesty's reign; and yet so wasteful and destructive is the present system of management in those forests, that the general quantity of timber in them lessens every year.

'We are aware that there have been similar complaints, and apprehensions of a want of naval timber, in every age, from very early times; and it may therefore probably be supposed, that the danger is not more real now than it has formerly been: It may be imagined that if there be an increased demand for naval timber, as that demand must necessarily add to the price, and thereby give greater encouragement to importation and planting, there can be no reason to apprehend that where industry is so general, and property so secure, as they are in this country, an ample supply will not always be obtained from private property, or from general commerce.

'It will be found, however, that this principle does not hold in the case of naval timber: The great addition to the navy and commerce of Great Britain, with the rapid increase of the valuable business of ship building in this country, since the close of the last war, and since the employment of American-built ships in our trade has been restricted, are circumstances which render any other evidence of an immense additional demand for naval timber unnecessary; and our information, as to the reality of the general decrease of timber, is too certain to admit of any doubt. The Commissioners of the Navy having, one year with another, been furnished with no more than 2,000 loads of timber from His Majesty's forests, have purchased all the rest, being about twenty-three thousand loads, from individuals in this country; no part of the rough timber being now imported. A Board which has such ample means of acquiring information, by its numerous and extensive transactions in the purchase of timber, and whose attention is peculiarly directed to that object, cannot be deceived in this particular; and our information from that Board is corroborated, not only by the reports of our surveyors from every part of England, and by the answers to all our enquiries, but also by the opinions of the best authors who have written on the subject.

'It is found, therefore, from experience, that an addition to the demand for naval timber does not produce a proportional supply from private property; and the reason is obvious: an oak must grow an hundred years, or more, before it comes to maturity; but the profits arising from tillage or pasture are more certain and immediate, and perhaps as great: It cannot, therefore, be expected that many private individuals will lay out money on the expectation of advantages which they themselves can have no chance to enjoy: Commerce and industry seek for, and are supported by, speedy returns of gain, however small; and the more generally the commercial spirit shall prevail in this country, the less probability is there that planting of woods, for the advantages of posterity, will be preferred to the immediate profits of agriculture.

'It is accordingly in the northern, or mountainous parts of the Kingdom chiefly, and on land unfit for tillage, where any great plantations have lately been made; and these are mostly of fir: But the oak, to become great timber, requires the strongest and deepest soil, which being also the most profitable for Agriculture, is the least likely to be employed by individuals in raising timber.

'For the remedy or prevention of this scarcity, which has so long been apprehended, various plans have, at different periods, been adopted, or recommended. In early times, recourse was had to the narrow system of putting restraints on the use and management of private property: In the reign of Henry VIII a law was made, by which it is enacted, "That Twelve Standils or Storers, likely to become Timber Trees, shall be left on every acre of Wood or Underwood that shall be felled at or under 24 years Growth; the turning Wood Land into Tillage is prohibited; and whenever any Wood is cut, it must be immediately enclosed, and the young Spring of Wood protected for Seven Years; and Penalties are appointed for every Transgression against this Law." And in the 13th of Elizabeth, there were further provisions relative to the Management of Woods on private estates.

'But these regulations have proved altogether ineffectual. The management of private property cannot any where be placed, with more safety and advantage to the public, than with the proprietors: The interference of Government, farther than in the protection of property, is always submitted to with reluctance, often evaded, and seldom productive of any benefit to the public.

'It is true that there is no kind of property that requires the protection of laws more than timber, which may easily, and in very little time, be hurt or destroyed, but requires a century to come to perfection. The penal laws relative to the destruction of trees should, for that reason, be rigidly enforced, and the punishments perhaps encreased: yet as all the expectation of advantage which the free use and the most entire command of the property can give, is found insufficient to induce men to plant, with a view to so distant a return, so much as the demand requires, Government should certainly not lessen that expectation by restraints on the use, or interference in the management, of the woods of individuals; and any laws which hold out such discouragements should, perhaps, be repealed.

'But though the leaving to every man the entire and uncontrolled use and management of his own woods, is the most likely way to encourage planting on private estates, yet we are very far from agreeing with those who think that Government may safely trust to the supply of timber which private estates and commerce will afford.

'Holland is an example, and perhaps the only one that can be given, of a country which, without forests of its own, belonging either to individuals or to the state, has been regularly supplied with naval timber through the medium of commerce; but the situation of Holland is very different from that of Great Britain. A state with little territory can have no other means of supply; and the great rivers which, after passing through an extensive continent in which there are many forests, fall into the sea in Holland, added to its vicinity to those Northern Countries which abound the most in wood, give Holland advantages in procuring timber by commerce, which no other country possesses in the same degree: But in this kingdom there are large tracts of land belonging to the Crown which cannot be applied to better uses; the British oak is of a superior quality to any that grows in those northern parts of Europe, from whence only we can be supplied without enormous expense. It is said too that timber is becoming scarce in those countries; and we certainly should not depend on other states for what is essential to our own defence.

'But if Government cannot with safety depend on the supplies from private estates in this kingdom, nor on what may be imported from abroad, neither ought it to trust to a sufficient supply for our navy from the royal forests, circumstanced as they now are, and while they remain under the present system of management.

'The improvident and often ill-defined grants made by the Crown in many of the forests, and the confused mixture of rights created by them, have the worst effect upon the property itself. The proprietor of the underwood must wish to prevent the growth of timber, by which his crop is diminished; and it is for their advantage of those to whom the herbage has been granted, that no wood should grow up of any kind: The whole is a perpetual struggle of jarring interests in which no party can improve his own share without hurting that of another.

'But the contest is very unequal: At a distance from the seat of Government the inhabitants and borderers on those extensive forests have the greatest temptations, as well as the best opportunities, to injure and encroach on the Property reserved by the Crown; and the Crown must find it extremely difficult to protect its remaining rights.

'Formerly, when the Crown Lands afforded the chief revenue by which the expense of Government was supported; when, to avoid the demand of aids from the people, which a failure in that revenue gave occasion for, resumptions of grants were not only common but popular; and when the forest laws were carried into full execution, there was little danger that the Crown would suffer a permanent loss of its landed property; for though the encroachments, devastation, and spoil in the forests were perhaps more rapid, in times of public disturbance, and during the reigns of weak or improvident princes, than they even now are, yet such was the power exercised by the Crown, that what was lost or granted away during a relaxed or profuse administration, was resumed, or amply compensated, by the first Monarch who gave attention to that part of his property: and whoever considers the resumption of grants, and the oppressive extensions of the forests in early times, or reads the Reports of Sir William Jones, of the Proceedings before the Earl of Holland; as Chief Justice in Eyre, in the reign of Charles I will see that there was formerly more danger to private property from the violent exertions of power, than to the property of the Crown by the encroachments of individuals.

'The situation now is very different: Private property, happily for this country, is in perfect security; but the property of the Crown in the forests is open to daily encroachments; and unless a stop shall soon be put to the progress of existing abuses, and some interruption given to intrusive possession, the greatest part of the timber now growing in the forests will be destroyed; and those rights which are at present retrievable, will be gradually lost.'

There is much that is fundamental to the whole problem of our woodlands and timber supplies here, and some passages in this document should be remembered at the present time.

Before discussing the consequences that followed upon the presentation of this Report, it is interesting to examine one instance of what private enterprise was doing in 'the northern or mountainous parts of the Kingdom'. This has already been briefly referred to and concerns how, principally owing to the enterprise of the Dukes of Atholl, the larch was raised from an insignificant ornamental tree to one of economic consequence. An account of what the Dukes did was reprinted in Loudon's *Arboretum*.

Between 1740 and 1750 Duke James planted 350 larches at Dunkeld, at 180 feet above sea level, and 873 at Blair, up to 560 feet above sea level. These plantations were within the ornamental grounds of Dunkeld House and Atholl House respectively, the trees being set in rows widely apart, and apparently grown not primarily for timber, but as a trial with a then little-known species. In 1759, the Duke planted 700 larches mixed with other kinds of tree up the face of a hill between 200 and 400 feet above sea level with the purpose of trying them out as timber producers. The ground consisted of crumbling rock and was of little value; it has been described as the first attempt at mountain planting in Scotland. The Duke died in 1764 without doing any more planting, but having discovered that the timber of even his young trees was good quality.

His successor, John, the third Duke, 'first conceived the idea of planting larch by itself as a forest tree, and of planting the sides of the hills about Dunkeld'. He began this work in 1768, now planting up to 600 feet above sea level and above Duke James's plantations, on land that was agriculturally worthless. He enclosed for this undertaking (which included mixed plantations) a total of 665 acres at Dunkeld and Blair, of which, at his death in 1774, 410 acres had been planted.

His plan was hindered by the shortage, and consequent high cost, of seedlings. Trees on the estate began coning at the time he started operations, but provided only 1,000 plants in a season. He was only able to buy, at 6d per plant, enough larches to plant fifty to the Scots acre out of the total of 4,000 trees to the Scots acre that it was then the practice to plant. The remainder were largely Scots pine, which he planted from the 600 feet limit of the larch up to 900 feet. He was also faced with difficulties due to inadequate clearing of the ground on which broom, furze, juniper and heather prospered, and he was away from Scotland a good deal. He had, however, made considerable progress and the experience that he gained no doubt benefited his son, who continued the planting on an even greater scale when he succeeded in 1774. Like his father, he was hindered by shortage of young plants, and did not complete the plan his father intended until 1783, by which time he had succeeded in obtaining only 279,000 plants. By then, 'observing the rapid growth and hardy nature of the larch tree, the duke determined on extending the sphere of its occupation to the steep acclivities of mountains of greater altitude than any that had yet been tried. Hitherto the larch had chiefly been planted along with other trees; but the duke enclosed a space including twenty-nine acres, on the rugged summit of Craig-y-barns, and planted a strip consisting entirely of larch, among the crevices and hollows of the rocks, where the least soil could be found. At this elevation, none of the larger kinds of natural plants grew, so that the ground required no previous preparation of clearing.' Here was, indeed, a revolution in British forestry technique. The economics of the operation were considerably affected when the price of plants shortly fell from 6d a plant to 35s per thousand, while labour costs remained for a while unchanged. Later, his planting costs increased, partly because he was removing Scots pine and replacing it with larch.

Duke John's operations were rapidly and widely extended. From 1816 he only planted larch pure, and from that year until 1826 he planted only a few thousand short of ten million of them. Careful records were kept from the earliest plantings; the three dukes between them (from 1738 to 1826) planted 14,096,719 trees, covering, making an allowance for the trees planted in mixture, 10,324 imperial acres.

The example set was inevitably followed by other landowners in the north, and within the century the mountain landscape was greatly changed, a change of far greater magnitude than anything achieved by the 'improvers'.

Elsewhere, larch was also planted. Thomas Johnes made a very extensive plantation at Hafod, in Cardiganshire. A Mr Thomas White planted a large number, mixed with other trees, at Batsfield in Durham, in 1786, and was awarded a Royal Society of Arts premium, which Society, as already mentioned, encouraged the planting of this tree. That was in 1788, when it offered three gold medals and a premium of £30. Loudon states that by the beginning of the nineteenth century its merits had become so widely known that it was more extensively planted than any other tree, not even excepting the oak. In his *Arboretum* he devotes no fewer than fifty pages to the European larch. This compares with one hundred and twelve given to the two British oaks.

Alas this development, which occurred even while the Commissioners were reporting, and although larch was becoming known as a highly valued timber for the hulls of boats (by 1819 the Duke of Atholl sold larch to Boulton and Watt for the building of steam boats), did not supply the massive timbers required by the Navy and provided only by old oak. However, in their Eleventh Report (1792) they point out that the demands for oak were in some ways lessening: 'Probably even within the last forty years, the consumption of oak timber in buildings, in many parts of England, has decreased. The improvements in roads, and inland navigation, which enable the internal parts of the country to send their oak to the dockyards, afford them at the same time the means of importing, at less expense, foreign fir timber, which answers most of the purposes of house building perhaps as well as oak. . . .

'. . . The same improvements in roads and canals having rendered the use of coal more general, less wood or timber is now probably consumed for fuel, and the art of charring pit coal, lately discovered, has prevented the consumption of wood and timber in the smelting of iron from being so very great, as, from the prodigious increase of that manufacture, it must otherwise have been.

'But, on the other hand, the consumption of timber in mill work, engines and machinery of various kinds, in lighters, barges and boats, piers, bridges, wharfs, locks and sluices, in wheelwrights and cooper's work, park pales, posts and rails, and many other articles which fir timber is not fit for, and depend on the population, manufacturers, commerce, agriculture, and wealth of the country, is increased to such a degree, as we apprehend at least counterbalancing the saving occasioned by the disuse of oak for house-building or other domestic uses.' Not included in that list were the smaller merchant ships, which used lesser timbers and so prevented oaks maturing to naval size. On occasion, their building was restricted.

The answer was to improve the long neglected silviculture of oak in the Royal forests. But how to do this? The experts were approached: 'their opinions differ no less as to the mode of managing woods; some recommend the bringing up of trees of different ages in the same wood, and as often as any of them arrive at maturity, to fell those trees, and leave the rest standing, to be cut in succession; while other persons of equal skill advise, that when the greater number of trees in the same wood arrive at their full size, the whole should be cut down, and the ground should be completely cleared and re-planted.'

Eventually it was recommended that on good ground, the objective being great timber, the method to be followed was that the young trees should be regularly thinned out, the finest being preserved without regard to the underwood, leaving a final crop of forty trees to the acre.

There are many sidelights on the uses of timber to be found in the document. For instance, serious experiments were being carried out to cut down the waste of good timber by revising design, and by the discovery that it was, for example, also caused by the fact that oak chips were a valuable perquisite for the shipwright. We learn that larch was being tried experimentally as a replacement: it matured in fifty or sixty years, against at least a century needed for oak. The East India Company was already using iron 'knees' in its new ships and imported exotic timbers were proving satisfactory.

However, all the suggestions made by the Commissioners needed time to be put into practice. When they finished their deliberations, the Government was distracted by the outbreak of the French Revolutionary wars and their immediate problems. The proposals of the Commissioners were put on one side. Meanwhile, the shortage became more acute.

NOVELTIES

The eighteenth was a century during which there were many introductions of trees from abroad. By far the largest proportion came from eastern North America, followed by the continent of Europe, with others coming from Chile, China, Japan, Siberia and even Aleppo. Loudon gives this total as 113 species, most of which are now quite common in collections, and of which several have, in varying degrees and localities, become a part of the British scene.

The first to come, though not a rarity, has never been the success – and economically valuable tree – that it might have been. *Pinus strobus*, the eastern white pine, ranges from the eastern and north-eastern states of the United States through south-eastern Canada as far north as Newfoundland. It was soon discovered to be a highly valuable timber tree. H. J. Elwes quotes: 'Great fleets of ships and long railroads have been built to transport the lumber sawn from its mighty trunks, men have grown rich by destroying it, building cities to supply the needs of their traffic, and seeing them languish as the forests disappear.'

Long before that, the timber was of great importance to the English. By 1652 it was available in Europe and, as has already been mentioned, we were using it for masts. It was not so strong as our native pine, but was in such lengths as to make possible the longest masts in one piece.

It is said, with little authority, that it was first grown at Badminton, by the Duchess of Beaufort in 1705. The English name, Weymouth pine, is due to the large number planted by Lord Weymouth at Longleat, Wiltshire, where by 1730 it had produced ripe seed for several years; it does, however, carry fertile seed as early as twenty or so years old.

Unfortunately, with us the Weymouth pine has never been satisfactory, except very locally, as a timber producer. Further, in 1892 it was first noted that trees were being attacked by a blister rust fungus which had as its alternate host current bushes. Subsequently, it has made the large-scale cultivation of this beautiful tree very difficult, though strains that are immune may exist.

The deciduous Turkey oak, *Quercus cerris*, is now one of our common ornamental trees and enters the British flora as a naturalised alien, particularly in the southern and midland counties. It is easily distinguished from out native oaks by the long, loose scales surrounding the buds, and the long, pointed scales of the acorn cup. The leaves are deeply cut. It grows naturally in southern Europe, particularly the Balkans, Syria, and Asia Minor. Evelyn did no more than mention an oak called *Cerris*, but says nothing about it growing here. It is, in fact, difficult to be precise about the date of introduction, and that given by Loudon, 1735, is usually accepted. In the latter part of that century it was widely planted, particularly in the south-west, presumably because it was a much faster growing tree than our native oaks and would supply good timber quickly. The wood is, however, of poor quality, and for long this oak has only been cultivated as a particularly handsome ornamental tree, frequently found in parks. The name *cerris* is an ancient classical one, and the English epithet 'Turkey' is rather puzzling; it was apparently first called the Burgundy oak.

Next in order of introduction came the northern red oak (*Quercus borealis*), which grows over a big area in the north-eastern states of the U.S.A., spreading into south-east Canada. It is unusual in being one of the very few of the numerous North American oaks which will thrive in the British Isles, where it is common as an ornamental tree and is to some extent planted in our forests, where it produces tolerably good timber on light soils unsuited to our native oaks.

There has been in the past great confusion over this tree, particularly – and not surprisingly – with *Q. rubra*, the red or Spanish oak, which has a more southerly distribution and is unsatisfactory in the British Isles. Further, it is a very variable tree and the form of the larger leaves and acorns has even earned a name of its own, *Q. maxima*. It has been discovered, however, that acorns from this produce a certain amount of seedlings with the smaller leaves and acorns of a type formerly restricted by botanists to *Q. borealis*. This has solved the problem of the date of its introduction to England, which is given as prior to 1739 for the kind formerly classified as *maxima* and 1800 for the type – the former by some person unknown, the latter by John Fraser, a Scot who came to London where he first set up as a draper and then, his interest having turned to botany, became a plant collector.

Red oak was cultivated as a timber-producing tree in Holland, Belgium and Germany with some success before British forest plantations were made; some at least of our best forest trees have been raised from acorns from these continental trees. The tree is, compared with our native oaks, much more slender and graceful in form, and the leaves colour from a rich brown to dull red in autumn. The opening leaves are a lovely shade of yellow-green.

In the last few decades it has been planted on the margins of a number of our forests to give variety and autumn colours, and it is therefore playing an increasing part in the British forestry scenery.

The weeping willows, on the contrary, take no part in our forest scenery and are without economic value. Instead, their Rapunzle-like tresses decorate miles of our river banks and are found drooping over countless ornamental waters with which our islands are blessed.

The story of our weeping willows (for there are several of them) begins – presumably – with Psalm 137: 'By the waters of Babylon, there we sat down, yea we wept, when we remembered Zion. We hanged our harps, upon the willows in the midst thereof.'

The learned assert that the tree in question was not a willow, but *Populus euphratica*; the successful hanging of a harp on the weeping willows we know would in any case be rather difficult. But this sad happening to the tribes of Israel must surely be responsible for the sadness long associated with willows in general, which is found in English literature as far back as the sixteenth century – particularly the refrain 'willow, willow, willow'.

More precise early examples come from Francis Pilkington, of about 1605:

> *I sigh, as sure to wear the fruit*
> *Of the willow tree*
> *I sigh, as sure to loose my suit;*
> *For it may not be.*

Or from William Browne, in about 1613:

> *And trees whose tears their loss commiserate . . .*
> *And willow for the forlorn paramour.*

None of these trees can have been the weeping willow that we know. A very early English reference to what must be this is found in Sir George Wheler's record of his travels. In October, 1675, he was at Brusa in Asia Minor when 'Dr Covel made me take notice of a willow-tree, whose large branches were so limber, that they bend down to the ground, from a good high-pollard, and naturally make a curious shady bower around it.' He adds that the leaf resembled our common osier.

It is generally believed that the French naturalist J. P. de Tournefort brought the tree to Europe at the end of the seventeenth century. Peter Collinson, the distinguished Quaker botanist, wrote that he first saw it in 1748, growing in the Twickenham garden of Mr Vernon, a Turkey merchant, who had brought it in about 1730 from the banks of the River Euphrates. It was soon widely planted – for example, it is seen in Zoffany's painting of *The Garricks entertaining Dr Johnson* (the artist died in 1779). There is a charming story, too, of how Alexander Pope was with Lady Suffolk when he observed that a parcel she had received from Spain (or some say Turkey) was bound with withies. One of these he rooted as a cutting, and it proved to be a weeping willow. This story, however, did not originate until 1801.

A remarkable story concerning a weeping willow is told by John Smith of Kew Gardens. A tree had been planted by Napoleon's grave on St Helena, the species having been introduced to the island in 1810 by General Beatson.[1] In 1825 a twig from it was brought to Kew. On one Sunday the crowd coming to see this novelty was so great that their pressure burst open the gates, 'the result being bruises and flattened hats and bonnets'. This specimen grew in the gardens until 1867, when it was cut down during alterations. Probably many British trees were propagated by snippings surreptitiously taken

The true *Salix babylonica* probably originated in central and southern China. It is not an entirely hardy tree in this country, seldom long-lived and is scarce. Today, many of our weeping willows are hardier hybrids of unknown origin. By far the commonest one of these is the beautiful yellow-twigged tree known as *Salix alba* 'Tristis', introduced into this country in 1888 by the German nursery firm of Späth.

As an extreme contrast with the weeping willow, and a notable exclamation mark in our scenery, is the Lombardy poplar (Plate 36). It is now claimed that it is a true species, a native of Russian central Asia and

[1] Recent examination has shown this to be the true *Salix babylonica* (*Gardener's Chronicle*, 19th September, 1964).

Afghanistan, named *Populus italica*. There are those who consider it to be a sport of the true black poplar from southern Europe (*P. nigra*), a view substantiated by the report[1] of a Lombardy in New Zealand, which had reverted to the normal form. This argument is fortified by the fact that only the male form, carrying red pollen-bearing catkins in spring, of the true Lombardy is known. (Other fastigiate poplars carrying female flowers exist, but they differ from the Lombardy and are of bushier growth.) The tree is therefore propagated by cuttings, which root very easily.

This poplar was reputedly widely planted on riversides in Italy, particularly, it is said, in Lombardy – a statement rather contradicted by the knowledgeable Arthur Young in 1789 when he observed that they were very scarce in that countryside. It is often claimed to have been first brought to England from Turin by our ambassador there, the Earl of Rochford, and planted at his home, St Osyth's Priory, Essex, in 1758. The trees are still there. In 1835, however, there was, on the site of Archibald, Duke of Argyle's famous collection of trees – he died in 1761 – at Whitton, a Lombardy of 115 feet high. This equals in height the tallest known specimen today, and the Duke may well have been the original introducer.

The timber of the Lombardy is of no value, On the other hand, that of the poplar known incongruously as the black Italian or Canadian poplar (botanically *P. serotina*, the late-leafing poplar – an accurate description) was one of the first to be grown on a large scale for timber suitable for pulp, matches, chip-baskets and other specialised markets. It is also one of the few timber trees that a man may plant and harvest within his own lifetime, so quickly does it grow. It is one of a series of hybrids sometimes called *euramerica*, one of whose parents is the Eastern Cottonwood (*P. deltoides*) which has an exceptionally wide range in eastern North America and is consequently a very variable tree. The other in this case is the European *P. nigra*. This cross of species from the Old and New Worlds accounts for its two English names. When and where the cross occurred is not known, but it existed in Europe before 1755, when the French botanist Duhamel du Monceau described it. It is probable that the hybrid arose naturally in Europe and was then taken to North America, and from Canada brought to England in 1772. It was popularised by the nurserymen, Archibald Dickson and Co., of Hasendeanburn in Scotland,

---

[1] *Kew Bulletin*, 1929.

and widely planted, first in the north of the British Isles, from about 1778 onwards.

Today, this tall tree (it has reached 140 feet) with few, but heavy limbs, generally sloping away from the prevailing wind, still black and bare of leaves (though covered with long crimson catkins in late March – only the male form is known) after most trees are in leaf, is a common sight in the landscape, often carrying bushes of mistletoe, usually in small groups. In the last few decades it and similar timber-producing hybrid poplars have been widely planted in fertile land, regularly spaced with the lower branches kept pruned away. On occasion, puss-moth caterpillars can reach plague proportions and defoliate these plantations.

In 1759 another tree with the epithet 'black' had been introduced from Corsica. It was first considered a variety of the Scots pine, and so named *Pinus sylvestris var. maritima*. Almost at once it was recognised as a form of the true black pine, *P. nigra*. This began its career of bewildering name changing, *P. nigra maritima* being that at the moment in vogue with the authorities at Kew, though the varietal epithets *calabrica* and *poiretiana* are still used. The original attribution to Scots pine, combined with 'black', gives a clue to the appearance of this tree. It is a large, very erect (even in windy places) and rather sombre tree, at once differentiated from the Scots by the absence of reddish bark in the upper part. It was first grown for ornament until its hardiness, tolerance of wide variation in soils and reasonably good timber were appreciated. It has been extensively used in forestry since about 1870, often to stabilise coastal dune sites. It is the major tree of Corsica, whose woods are beautifully illustrated in Edward Lear's book on that island.

Another eighteenth-century discovery was the Florence Court yew, already described among our native trees.

The last introduction of importance during this century was the monkey-puzzle, *Araucaria araucana*. A very few were brought here by Archibald Menzies in 1795, but as for some fifty years it was such a rarity, this is really one of the Victorians, and will be discussed when that period is reached.

CHAPTER SIX

The Rise of the Picturesque

HUMPHRY REPTON (1725–1818) was literally the successor to Brown. His only qualifications for planning the planting of thousands of trees and appreciably modifying the landscape were that he was a talented, but very minor, water-colour painter, an antiquarian, and had some knowledge of botany. In all these matters he was an amateur. He had good social connections in East Anglia, and had a little administrative experience in Ireland unexpectedly thrust on him. Failure in a business venture left him in financial difficulties, with a family to support. This happened at the time of Brown's death.

Though Brown left behind a number of assistants and imitators, Repton almost at a moment's notice decided that his mantle would rest well on his shoulders (an opinion with which Brown's son agreed, for he lent him his father's plans), advised his estate-owning friends that he was setting up as an 'improver' of landscapes – the term seems particularly connected with him – and within a few years had among his clientele some of the most distinguished landowners in the country (Plate 37). To those to whom he recommended that new, modern buildings were desirable, he presented John Nash (1752–1835), then a little-known provincial architect, as the man to provide them.[1]

Repton designed his 'improvements' in an original manner. He would make a careful study of the estate and a series of sketches as it then was. He would next work out the necessary 'improvements', and produce imaginary drawings of the place after the requisite changes had been made and matured. These were arranged to fold over his first figures, so that the

[1] Brown himself designed buildings, but later put much architectural work in the hands of his son-in-law, Henry Holland (1745–1806).

client would study the scene 'before and after'. The drawings were bound in red-covered books, the 'red books' that are still in the archives of many an old estate. This method was very much more effective than the usual method of preparing plans, giving an immediate picture of the change to the most incompetent map-reader.

There are many more red books in existence than estates that Repton actually improved. Sometimes the client would take no further action – or pass them on to some minor landscapers who carried out Repton's suggestions in an inferior manner.

Repton, unlike his predecessors, wrote freely on his theory and practice. His published books, some delightfully illustrated in colour, were there for all to use. In old age, therefore, he was to find his name attached to scenes for which he was not responsible.

Even so, whether genuine or not, the calm, Reptonian manner, more imaginative than that of Brown, but less brilliant in the management of water, with cattle[1] quietly grazing under the now aged clumps and dotted individual trees, the whole still probably surrounded by that belt of woodland that his critics were later to decry, is still fortunately seen in our countryside (Plate 38).

Unlike Brown, whose designs were, as has been well said, rather like a theatrical set to be viewed principally from the house, Repton (and all the 'red books' show this) designed his landscapes as a setting for the house itself, and furthermore, as a setting which, as one approached the mansion, impressed the visitor – or even passer-by – with the right degree of social status and wealth of the owner. In his writing, he was so frank about this that it cannot really be called snobbery or servility. It was, to him, a matter of social significance. Repton's enemies were later to make great play with this.

If we can rely on Jane Austen's novels as evidence, and indeed Cowper,[2] Repton and his amateur imitators dealt a final blow to the formal garden, for, unlike Brown who worked on the great estates, they – particularly the imitators – carried their 'improvements' to the smaller country residences.

The first critic of the Brownian/Reptonian scene and advocate of the

---

[1] The Rev. William Gilpin wrote a dissertation to prove that the cow in a landscape was more picturesque than the horse.

[2] The 'lime colonnade' at Weston was felled in 1788 because the improvers considered it rectilinear: 'it is a wonder they do not quarrel with a sunbeam', wrote the poet to Lady Hesketh.

49. Victorian ornamental woodland; Glendurgan, Cornwall.

50. Victorian conifers and water; Dropmore, Buckinghamshire.

51. Victorian conifers, formally and informally planted; Castlewellan.

52. Brewer's Spruce; Westonbirt, Gloucestershire.

picturesque was Richard Payne Knight (1750–1824), whose 'didactic poem' *The Landscape* was published in 1794 (Plate 39). In 1805 he published *An Analytical Enquiry Into the Principles of Taste*.

The Knights were ironmasters in Shropshire who had followed the timber they needed into north Herefordshire, where they had considerable estates. Richard Payne, an 'epicurean philosopher . . . a sensualist in all ways, but a quiet and self-educated scholar',[1] was traveller, antiquarian, an eminent collector of antiquities and a numismatist who left his remarkable collections to the British Museum. In 1774 he began to build Downton Castle, in a situation of romantic beauty above the limestone gorge through which cuts the River Teme to enter calmer ground, where incidentally it flows around Oakly Park, landscaped by Brown. The Castle was an irregular, castellated building – a pioneer of its strange type – with an interior that is 'beautifully classical'. The key to this ambiguity is given in his own writings, and foreshadows, as does the whole of this late eighteenth-century picturesque mode, the logic of the Victorian manner of aesthetic confusion:

'. . . the architecture of the Gothic castles, as they are called, is of Grecian or Roman origin; but, if it were not, there could be no impropriety in employing the elegance of Grecian taste and science, either in the external forms and proportions, or interior decorations of houses built in that style: for, surely, there can be no blameable consistency in uniting the different improvements of different ages and countries in the same object; providing they are really improvements, and contribute to rendering it perfect.'

Here is the beginning of that historically founded confused eclecticism which was to produce also such majestic planting. Within a few decades these 'castles' – such as Eastnor, Penrhyn, Eridge and Castlewellan – were surrounded with the recently introduced conifers; it is within their environs that some of the finest specimens now stand.

Payne Knight was himself no planter, though his footnotes in *The Landscape* show him to have had an unusual knowledge of trees. He did not live long at Downton, but passed it over to his brother, Thomas Andrew (1759–1834), an outstanding pioneer in horticulture and kindred matters, particularly genetics.

Payne Knight's vision of the picturesque can be epitomised by two quotations attacking the work of Brown and his disciple Repton. After praising Claude's 'prospect wide', where towers and temples moulder to decay,

---

[1] *The Greville Memoirs*, 1839.

And the soft distance, melting from the eye
Dissolves its forms into the azure sky . . .

as well as Hobbema's village mills, great Salvator's mountains, the ivy'd
cottage of Ostade, Waterloe's copse, and Ruysdael's low cascade, he
launches out:

. . . See yon fantastic band,
With charts, pedometers, and rules in hand,
Advance triumphant, and alike lay waste
The forms of nature, and the works of taste!
T'improve, adorn, and polish, they profess;
But shave the goddess, whom they come to dress;

Level each broken bank and shaggy mound,
And fashion all to one unvaried round;
One even round, that ever greatly flows,
Nor forms abrupt, nor broken colours knows;
But wrapt all o'er in everlasting green,
Makes one dull, vapid, smooth and tranquil scene . . .

Hence, hence, thou haggard fiend, however call'd,
Thin, meagre genius of the bare and bald;
Thy spade and mattock here at length lay down,
And follow to the tomb thy fav'rite Brown. . . .

Or again, instead of Brown's spacious and unencumbered views from the
house:

The bright acacia, and the vivid plane,
The rich laburnum with its golden chain;
And all the variegated flow'ring race,
That deck the garden, and the shrubb'ry grace,
Should near to buildings, or to water grow
When bright reflections beam with equal glow,
And blending vivid tints with vivid light,
The whole in brilliant harmony unite . . .

Knight was, apparently unknowingly, going back to Hamilton's
Painshill (but without ornamental buildings, which he deplored) and at
the same time pointing the way forward to romanticism and ultimately
such remarkable ornamental woodlands as Westonbirt, Sheffield Park and
to other twentieth-century landscapes.

The Landscape was 'addressed to Uvedale Price, Esq.', who in the same year published *An Essay on the Picturesque, as compared with the Sublime and the Beautiful; and on the use of studying pictures for the purpose of improving rural landscape.* This work was developed in subsequent editions, and was of considerable consequence.

Edmund Burke's *Philosophical Inquiry into . . . the Sublime and Beautiful* is so often referred to as having affected the landscape art, and Shenstone in particular – though it was only published in 1756, seven years before Shenstone's death and after his garden had been completed – that it might be well to quote Burke's summaries of those attributes in an attempt to clarify what was originally meant by the picturesque,[1] subsequently a term so widely used.

'The passion called up by the great and the *sublime* in nature, when those causes operate most powerfully, is astonishment; and astonishment is that state of the soul, in which all its motions are suspended, with some degree of horror. In this case the mind is so entirely filled with its object, that it cannot entertain any other, nor by consequence reason on that object which employs it.

'Hence arises the great power of the sublime, that, far from being produced from them, it anticipates our reasonings, and hurries us on by an irresistible force.

'Astonishment, as I have said, is the effect of the sublime in its highest degree; the inferior effects are admiration, reverence and respect.

'On the whole, the qualities of beauty, as they are merely sensible qualities, are the following: First, to be comparatively small. Secondly, to be smooth. Thirdly, to have a variety in the direction of the parts; but, fourthly, to have those parts not angular, but melted as it were into each other. Fifthly, to be of delicate frame, without any appearance of strength. Sixthly, to have its colour clear and strong, but not very strong and glaring, or if it should have any glaring colouring, to have it diversified with others.

'These are, I believe, the properties on which beauty depends; properties that operate by nature, and are less liable to be altered by caprice, or confounded by a diversity of tastes, than any other.'

Price, while agreeing with Burke on these points, went further. 'The picturesque,' he wrote, 'is much less obvious, less generally attractive, and had been totally neglected and despised by professional improvers.'[2]

---

[1] The word *pittoresque*, first admitted by the French Academy in 1731, has a dissimilar meaning to picturesque as used here.

[2] Brown and Repton in particular. Of the former's lake at Blenheim he quotes an

His essays brought about some surprisingly – to us – violent literary attacks upon him. Repton answered reasonably, and within a few years moved appreciably towards his views. Price greatly influenced Loudon, Steuart, Sir Walter Scott, Elizabeth Barrett Browning, and others who helped to form nineteenth-century taste.

Sir Uvedale Price (1747–1829), first baronet, with an ancestry which had mixed Welsh origins with the English aristocracy, inherited the Foxley estate, romantically set among hills above the Wye near Hereford – a situation, like Downton, by nature singularly unlike any landscape that Brown conceived.[1]

'He was a travelled and cultured man, an admirer of Reynolds' *Discourses* (Reynolds painted his wife) and friendly with Lawrence, who painted his portrait and inherited an interest in the arts and sciences from his father, Robert, who was patron and instructor of the Oxford painter, Malchair, and friend of the scholar Benjamin Stillingfleet.'[2]

The house at Foxley was built in 1717, surrounded with walled gardens and terraces typical of the period; possibly, too, there were remains of the garden of an earlier house. He wrote his essays feelingly, from having done himself what he now condemned in others, namely demolished this old-fashioned garden. 'I destroyed it, not from disliking it; on the contrary, it was a sacrifice I made against my own sensations, to the prevailing opinion. I doomed it and all its embellishments, with which I had formed such an early connection, to sudden and total destruction; probably much upon the same idea, as many a man of careless, unreflecting, unfeeling good-nature, thought it his duty to vote for demolishing towns, provinces, and their inhabitants, in America; like me (but how different the scale and interest!) they chose to admit it as a principle, that whatever obstructed the prevailing system, must be thrown down – all laid prostrate: no medium, no conciliatory methods tried, but that whatever might follow, destruction must precede.'

Price's essays are evocative of the past and look far into the future: he suggested the planting of exotics in remote parts of the grounds, for 'there

---

opinion that there was not a housemaid in the palace to whom the idea would have not immediately occurred. Repton he accedes to be deservedly at the head of his profession. Kent he considers feeble.

[1] Brown's two Herefordshire landscapes, Moccas, alongside the Wye, and Berrington, are significantly on naturally level, park-like terrain.

[2] Ian Fleming-Williams *in lit.*

seems to be no reason against familiarising our eyes to a mixture of the most beautiful exotics where the climate will suit them.'

He was perspicacious, for example regretting that Vanbrugh 'did not turn his thoughts towards the embellishments of the garden, as far as they might serve to accompany his architecture; which, though above all others, open to criticism, is above most others, striking in its effects. A garden of Vanbrugh's, even in idea, will probably excite as much ridicule as his real buildings have done, and none ever excited more: but I am convinced that he would have struck out many peculiar and characteristic effects; and that a landscaper-gardener, who really deserved that name, would have touched with caution what he had done, and would have availed himself of many parts of such a garden.'

The leaving undisturbed of fine old trees, and the making of new plantations, to give an effect of natural vigour, even roughness and subtle variety as opposed to Brown and Repton's suavity, were a great part of his thesis. He was an acute observer of the visual qualities of trees: 'the rugged old oak, or knotty wyche elm, . . . are picturesque; nor is it necessary they should be of great bulk; it is sufficient if they are rough, mossy, with a character of age, and with sudden variations in their forms. The limbs of huge trees, shattered by lightning or tempestuous winds, are in the highest degree picturesque; but whatever is caused by those dreaded powers of destruction, must always have a tincture of the sublime.'

Or:

'As the young ash (though at any age by no means a popular tree) is a favourite with painters, it must seem consistent to those who refer the term to art only, that I should deny it to be picturesque. . . . The young ash has every principle of beauty; freshness and delicacy of foliage, smoothness of bark, elegance of form; nor am I surprised that Virgil, whose peoetry has so much of those qualities, should call the ash the most beautiful tree in the woods; but when its own leaves are changed to the autumnal tint, and when contrasted with ruder or more massive shapes or colours, it becomes part of a picturesque circumstance, without changing its own nature.'

Loudon summarised Price's principles of design:

'Your [the landscape designer's] object is to produce beautiful landscapes. . . . But (at present) you produce very indifferent ones. The beauty of your scenes is not of so high a kind as that of nature. Examine her productions. To aid you in this examination, consult the opinions of those who have gone before you in the same study. Consult the works of painters, and learn the principles which guided them in their combinations of natural and artificial objects. Group your trees on the principles they do. Connect your masses as they do. In short, apply their principles of painting whenever you intend any imitation of nature; for the principles of nature and of painting are the same. Are we to apply them in every case? Are we to neglect regular beauty and utility? Certainly not; that would be inconsistent with common sense.'

The estate at Foxley is today richly wooded and of great beauty, but very different from Sir Uvedale's day. In 1837 a writer in *The Gardener's Magazine* remarked that under his son, Sir Robert, the place was undergoing an unending series of alterations. In 1855 the property was sold and a new house built (now destroyed). The surrounds are now dominated by magnificent conifers of that period.

It seems likely that Price advised a number of his friends about their gardens, and it is said that his brother, Major Price, was responsible for 'improvements' at Frogmore.

The effect on Repton of Knight's and Price's strictures was appreciable. In 1806 he replied in *An Enquiry Into The Changes of Taste in Landscape Gardening*, in which he stood up for the principles of Brown, which he considered his critics misapprehended, suggesting that he, Knight and Price were to a greater extent in agreement than they considered, but was adamant that the landscape painter had nothing in common with the landscape gardener. Nevertheless, in later designs, such as Endsleigh, above the River Tamar, he moved much closer to the Knight–Price school. Even in 1794 he had approved the avenue – as long as it curved.

A very considerable writer and critical commentator on the picturesque from the point of view of the tourist and connoisseur rather than that of the improver and planter was the Rev. William Gilpin (1724–1807), vicar of Boldre in Hampshire. His accounts of the tours that he made in the closing decades of the eighteenth century are of considerable interest, charmingly illustrated in aquatint. His *Remarks on Forest Scenery . . . Illustrated by the Scenes of the New-forest in Hampshire* (1791) is apposite to our purpose, and has already been quoted.

It is not insignificant that the period we have been discussing – from the mid-eighteenth to the opening years of the nineteenth century – is the age of great painters, who were so often profoundly concerned with trees. Wilson, Gainsborough, Stubbs, Taverner, the two Cozens, Sandby, Abbott, Varley, Cotman, and greatest of all, Constable, belatedly set a standard and tradition of profundity in the understanding of our trees that continued through countless charming Victorians down to such painters as John Nash. But to discuss this further is beyond our present purpose.[1]

As the reign of Victoria drew near, the English landscape garden was changing character. The Chevalier Charles Sckell, Director-General of Gardens in the Kingdom of Bavaria, writing in 1833, was concerned to point out both the differences of the German landscape style from the English, and the decline in purity of the English style.

'When I speak of the English style of gardening', he wrote, 'I mean only as it is exhibited in the grand and beautiful specimens which Brown, Kent and a few others, have left us; not that which, in these latter times, is so often practised in laying out garden grounds in England, and which has as little relation to the truly creative art of gardening, as the pictures of our modern painters have to the works of Raphael.

'Considered with respect to real landscape beauties, picturesque effects, and grand imaginative characteristics, the English garden style is, in the present style, markedly retrograde. When I was in England, in 1817, I found the gardens in the new English style, as I met with it, for the most part oppressed with the burthen of their own ornaments. The immense multitude of plants which, since the commencement of the present century, have been brought from all parts of the world to Europe, and more especially England,[2] supplies the landscape-gardener with an inexhaustible fund for decorating his grounds. There are thus to be found numerous varieties of trees and shrubs, which, either by their elegant growth, the picturesque disposition of their branches and foliage, or by their beautiful flowers, belong to the first class of ornaments for landscape-gardening.

'The palette of the landscape-painter, if I may so express myself, is now loaded with such a mass of colours and tints, that his means are superabundant, compared with the work of art that he has to create. . . .

'It might have been supposed that this richness of vegetation would be highly advantageous to landscape gardening in England, where, formerly the most classical modes of the natural garden style were to be found; and that it would have given immensely increased facilities to the artist for the execution of his work: but, according to my experience, I found

---

[1] I have done so briefly in *The Connoisseur Year Book*, 1960.

[2] During the first thirty years of the nineteenth century the number of new hardy trees and shrubs introduced into the British Isles was 699, against a total of 445 in the whole of the eighteenth!

quite the contrary. Amidst the disproportionate abundance of his materials, he knows not which to take first: one is scarcely chosen, when he is attracted to another; then to a third, a fourth, and so on. Each tree, and each shrub, has some particular charm to recommend it, and finally, that none may be lost, he grasps them all.

'Thus I found the English gardens a real chaos of unconnected beauties.'

That, then, most acutely stated, yet scarcely recognised until the end of the century, was the dilemma in which not only landscape, but the whole of gardening was – and indeed still largely is – placed. Hamilton at Painshill had early seen the possibilities of these new resources and used them well; the Hoares of Stourhead consistently and satisfactorily employed them. But today, the results of this nineteenth-century abundance are seen at their best in the avowed collections of the arboriculturists and connoisseurs, in their pineta and arboreta wherein acquisition and cultivation took precedence over taste and design.

At the period when Sckell wrote, though he did so partly in reflection, Repton, Price and Knight were dead; argument still continued over their views. The principal and most influential disputants and planters were, in the order of their birth, Sir Henry Steuart, of Alanton (1759–1836), William Sawrey Gilpin (1762–1843), Sir Walter Scott (1771–1832) and J. C. Loudon (1783–1843).

Steuart was an agriculturalist, arboriculturist and practical planter with views on design. His *Planter's Guide*, first published in 1828, was widely read. Of the numerous reviews, the one, unsigned, by Sir Walter Scott in the *Quarterly Review* of 1828 was the most consequential. It burgeoned into a discussion of garden history and the art of design, and an appraisal of Uvedale Price, whose picturesque theories he in general followed. His views, coming from so distinguished and popular an author – at that time in financial straits to which the grandeur of his plantings at Abbotsford had contributed – influenced public taste towards an even more romantic style of design.

One significant paragraph of this review must be quoted:

'Trees, therefore, remain the proper and most manageable material of picturesque improvement; and as trees and bushes can be raised almost anywhere – as by their presence they not only delight the eye, with their various forms and colours, but benefit the soil by their falling leaves, and improve the climate by their shelter, there is scarcely any property fitted for human habitation so utterly hopeless, as not to be rendered agreeable by extensive and judicious plantations.'

W. S. Gilpin is now forgotten. But unlike Steuart and Scott, he designed many gardens; the *Dictionary of National Biography* states that late in life he had a monopoly in landscape gardening. The son of Sawrey Gilpin, the animal painter, he was himself trained as an artist, taking to garden design though 'being very little conversant with flowers, their variety, culture, etc.'. In 1832 he published *Practical Hints for Landscape Gardening* (an enlarged edition was issued in 1835), delightfully illustrated by his own drawings; from this, we can learn the motives of his work.

His work has been little studied, though preliminary enquiries show that the claim that he carried out much landscaping is true,[1] so that his opinions justify mention.

He launches his *Practical Hints* thus:

'Agreeing fully with Sir Uvedale Price in his estimate of the requisites necessary to form a just taste in Landscape, I am emboldened to submit to the public my ideas upon the subject, having been bred to the study of Landscape Painting in the first instance, and having for many years applied the principles of painting to the improvement of real scenery.'

And he offers a few hints and warnings to an owner about to 'improve' his estate:

'I would recommend every proprietor of a place so circumstanced (if he become his own improver) to consult such pictures or prints as are applicable to the case. The "Liber Veritatis" of Claude, and the "Liber Studiorum" of Turner, will afford many examples to the purpose.

'The first caution, then, that I would suggest to a person not conversant with the study of landscape, is, not to remove any tree from the foreground till he has accurately observed the effect in winter, as well as in summer. Secondly, not to take away a tree merely upon account of its insignificance, not even its ugliness; as the beauty of the group may be made by that very tree. Thirdly, not to seek variety in the group from the differences which compose it, so much as from the general form of the whole.

'I would also suggest that round-headed trees are more picturesque than pointed ones; though, particularly in connection with buildings, the latter have frequently a good form; and, in some cases are most essentially useful. There is, I conceive, scarcely any tree that may not be advantageously used in the various combinations of form and colour: and, as immediately connected with buildings, I must say that the Lombardy poplar appears to me unjustly condemned; inasmuch as we have

1 For example, the framework in which Westonbirt is now set.

no tree that so well supplies the place of the cypress, in contrasting the horizontal lines of masonry, and giving occasional variety to the outline of the group. Portman Square affords an example in point: the horizontal lines of the houses on each side being broken and contrasted by the Lombardy poplars in the plantations; while the plantations themselves derive consequence and variety from the pointed form and superior height of the poplars: as, therefore, we cannot command the cypress of Italian growth, we find the Lombardy poplar its best representative.'

He follows Price and quite controverts the practice of Brown and Repton:

'One rule, indeed, may be universally laid down – never to plant a belt.

'In planting, the first care should be to connect the different plantations under one general intention; not to scatter them in detached spots, as it were at random, without any purpose of uniting them in composition.'

He gives good reasons for abolishing the ha-ha:

'Nor is it only in connection with houses of the old school that I should recommend a dwarf wall as the separating fence. In all houses which approach to the consequence of a mansion, if circumstances permit, I should wish its adoption: more particularly where it is essential that the uniformly inclined line of the scenery be interrupted as . . . a transparent fence will not restore the horizontal plane so necessary to the composition, as the sloping ground beyond will be seen through it.'

And finally, some interesting observations on tree form:

'The cedar of Lebanon adorns alike the gayer lawn of the Grecian mansion, and the deeper recesses of the manorial pile; and rash indeed must be the hand that would remove it from either. But, had I the choice between the Oak and the Elm as accompaniments, expecially to the manorial architecture, I should not hesitate to prefer the latter, as far more consonant with the general tone and sentiment of the building than the grandest Oak. Whoever has studied the perfect harmony that subsists between the "antique towers" of Eton College and the stately Elms which adorn its lawns will not hastily condemn this preference. The oaks of Blythfield Park could not produce that solemn grandeur which results from the deep tone of colour and monotonous masses of dense foliage of those Elms, whose grand, though simple outline, unbroken by any playful variety, are in unison with that contemplative solemnity with which the scene, and a consequent train of reflections, cannot fail to inspire the sensitive mind.

'The Scotch fir has, of late years, been planted merely as a nurse to the forest tree; but there are to be seen in many old places specimens which exhibit it in the very first rank of picturesque character, and approaching closely even to the grandeur of the cedar.

'Various opinions have been suggested, as to the cause of this obvious declension of a tree, still continued to be planted throughout all the varieties of soil and climate in Great Britain. . . .

'It would appear that, from whatever cause, the Scotch fir has, for many years, deteriorated both in its picturesque character and in its general estimation.'

The last observation is significant and shows Gilpin's powers of observation, for it is now well known that owing to the frequent introduction of unsuitable continental strains of the Scots pine there was great deterioration in the qualities typical of the native tree.

Loudon was the outstanding British authority on trees and arboriculture of his age. His *Arboretum et Fruticetum Britannicum* of 1838 is still a work of importance. It had a great effect in encouraging British arboriculture, which from his time became internationally famous as our timber-producing forestry declined. It is important to appreciate, however, that the revival of forestry in our islands was, as will be described later, based largely on this enthusiasm for the collection from abroad of exotic trees and their cultivation in our arboreta and pineta.

He has already been mentioned as an informed, critical, descriptive writer on the design of gardens. He himself designed but a few. In 1840 he published the complete works of Repton, yet always he was being pulled forward by contemporary forces. It was he who defined and advocated the gardenesque style: 'garden design which is best calculated to display the individual beauty of trees, shrubs, and plants; the smoothness and greenness of lawns; and the smooth surface, curved directions, dryness and firmness of gravel walks; in short, it is calculated for displaying the art of the gardener.' The technocrat, rather than the artist, is now moving towards his stultifying ascendancy.

It is interesting to examine at this stage the opinion in calm retrospect of a man of taste, and an active planter, Sir Henry Steuart, on Brown's work. In his *Planter's Guide* (1828) he reacts a little against Price's criticism:

'It is to be regretted that Sir Uvedale Price, in his very valuable *Essays on the Picturesque* (probably the most powerful example of controversial writing and acute criticism in the language), should have somewhat lessened their effect by personal sarcasm, and the bitterness of controversy.

As to Brown, he has not (according to the vulgar phrase) "left him the likeness of a dog"; and his conceit, his ignorance, his arrogance, his vanity (of all of which Brown had his full share), are blazoned forth in the most glaring colours. It is true, that to pull him down while in the zenith of his popularity, and afterwards to keep him down, surrounded as he was with followers and flatterers, required a vigorous and powerful arm like Sir Uvedale's; and no one, I think, will grudge the latter his complete triumph, or the castigation inflicted upon his opponent, considering the lasting benefit which his own labours have conferred on an elegant art, and in elevating the fame and character of the country. Still I cannot help thinking that poor Kent, though a man of rather limited genius, should have escaped more easily than he has done from the great critic's hands; since it is to him that we as clearly owe the art of landscape gardening, as we owe the saving of it from disgrace, and the placing it on just principles, to Sir Uvedale Price. May we not, then, ask, looking to the fine genius of the latter, *Tantanae animis coelestibus irae?*'

Of Thomas White,[1] the landscaper of his own estate, Alanton, he wrote:

'About 40 years since (*c.* 1780) when the style of Brown was in high fashion and repute, this place was modernised and laid out by an eminent landscape gardener, well known in Scotland, namely, Mr Thomas White, one of the most ingenious of his pupils. With a better education than his master could boast, with a more correct taste and a more vivid fancy, White had a juster discernment of the true style in which the principles of the artificial should be applied to the improvement of real landscape. He was a superior draughtsman, and possessed a thorough knowledge of the principles of design; and had it not been for the professional trammels by which he was confined, he probably would have anticipated, as well as illustrated in his own designs, those more correct notions of park scenery which Sir Uvedale Price and Mr Knight afterwards had the merit of bringing into notice. As it was, White rather yielded to, than approved of, the fashion of the day; accordingly, he gave a belt and clumps to all the new places he laid out, and sometimes to the old ones, which he so ingeniously improved.'

At this stage, too, we begin first to observe the highly emotional and sentimental (and surely not desirable) attitude towards trees that has since so unfortunately developed. This purple passage comes from the review of Steuart's book in *Blackwood's Magazine* of April, 1828:

---

[1] White worked in the north, living at Retford. He appears also to have provided designs at Houghton, Kilnwick, Grimston Garth and Burton Constable – all in Yorkshire.

Trees are indeed the glory, the beauty, and the delight of nature. . . . In what one imaginable attribute that it ought to possess, is a Tree, pray, deficient? Light, shade, shelter, coolness, freshness, musick, all the colours of the rainbow, dew and dreams dropping through their umbrageous twilight at eve or morn, – dropping direct, – soft, sweet, soothing and restorative, from Heaven. Without Trees, how, in the name of wonder, could we have had houses, ships, bridges, easy-chairs, or coffins, or almost any single one of the necessaries, conveniences, or comforts of life? Without Trees, one man might have been born with a silver spoon in his mouth, but not another with a wooden ladle. . . .'

CHAPTER SEVEN

Landscapes Beyond England

THE SPREAD of the English style of gardening to the European continent, and later, beyond, is a phenomenon in the fashion – probably psychology – of taste that has not been adequately studied. When Loudon compiled his *Encyclopaedia of Gardening* in 1827 he described the so-called English gardens, a number of which he visited, in most parts of Europe.

Georges Riat opens the fifth part of his *L'Art des Jardins* with the title *XVIIIe Siècle: Le Jardin Anglais* (the fourth having significantly been *XVIIe et XVIIIe Siècles: Le Jardin Français*) with a quotation from Taine's *Voyage en Italie* (1884):

'Les jardins anglais indignent l'avènement d'une autre race, la domination d'un autre goût, le règne d'une autre littérature, l'ascendant d'un autre esprit plus compréhensif, plus solitaire, plus aisément fatigué, plus tourné vers les choses dedans.'

Riat himself considered that the inspiration of Lorraine and Poussin, 'où les belles harmonies concouraient à une impression de calme et de majesté, où, dans l'air bleu, les personnes, les animaux, les choses vivaient d'une vie large et solenelle, en ces campagnes lumineuses' had been replaced by the romantic regions of Ireland, Scotland, Switzerland and Germany. Perhaps this presumably inherited misunderstanding helps to explain Walpole's outburst in 1771, when he wrote from Paris, 'English gardening gains ground here prodigiously. . . . I have literally seen one that is exactly like a tailor's paper of patterns. There is a Monsieur Boutin, who has tacked a piece of what he calls an English garden to a set of stone terraces, with steps of turf. There are three or four very high hills, almost as high as, and exactly in the shape of, a tansy pudding. You squeeze between these and a river, that is conducted at obtuse angles in a stone channel, and supplied by a pump; and when walnuts come in, I suppose it will be navigable. . . . They have translated Mr Whateley's book, and the Lord knows what barbarism is going to be laid at our door. This new *Anglomanie* will literally be *mad English*.'

Arthur Young, who had a subtle understanding of the English style, visited Queen Marie Antoinette's *Jardin Anglais* in 1788: 'it contains about 100 acres, disposed in the taste of what we read of in books of Chinese gardening, whence it is supposed the English style was taken. There is more of Sir William Chambers here than Mr Brown – more effort than nature – and more expence than taste. It is not easy to conceive any thing that art can introduce in a garden that is not here; woods, rocks, lawns, lakes, rivers, islands, cascades, grottos, walks, temples and even villages. There are parts of the design very pretty and well executed. The only fault is too much crowding; which has led to another, that of cutting the lawn by too many gravel walks, an error to be seen in almost every garden I have met with in France. But the glory of *La Petite Trianon* is the exotic trees and shrubs. The world has been successfully rifled to decorate it . . .'

Loudon, following his visit to Italy in 1819, wrote, 'there are various gardens pointed out to strangers as English, *veramente Inglese* . . . most of those which we visited were too much ornamented, and too full of walks, seats, arbors, and other ornaments, for that repose and simplicity which is essential to an English garden. Art, in most of these gardens, is as much avowed as in the French style; whereas, in the true English garden, though art is employed, yet it is not avowed and ostentatiously displayed; on the contrary, the grand object is to follow the directions of the Italians themselves, and study that the art *che tulto fa, nullo sei scopre.*'

Riat attributes this Chinese complexity of paths and smallness of scale to Chambers's influence. The *Dissertation*, not published until 1772, was, however, never translated into French, wheras Père Attiret's description of the Emperor of China's garden near Peking was in French and received in Paris in 1749, to be translated into English in 1752. Riat does not mention this among his list of literary influences, but surely it must have been great and later led to the odd term *anglo-chinois*, which did not originate in England, but is found in such works as Le Rouge's *Détails de Nouveaux Jardins à la mode* of 1766 onwards. He also points out that the sources of *le jardin anglais* in France, as in England, were literary. Among those he cites are Diderot's *Encyclopédie* (1750–81) 'diffusing among the public a taste for the observation of nature'. One quotation will suffice. Under

Jardin comes a caustic criticism of the then contemporary French style; referring scathingly to Chinese grotesques, Diderot continues:

'It is not so with a neighbouring nation, amongst whom gardens in good taste are as common as magnificent palaces are rare. In England, the walks, practicable in all weathers, seem made to be the sanctuary of a sweet and placid pleasure; the body is there relaxed, the mind diverted, the eyes are enchanted by the verdure of the turf. . . .

'Nature alone, modestly arrayed, and never made up, there spreads out her ornaments and benefits. How the fountains beget the shrubs and beautify them! How the shadows of the woods put the streams to beds of herbage! Let us call the birds in these places of delight; their concerts will draw man hither, and will form a hundred times better eulogy of a taste for sentiment, than marble and bronze whose display but produces a stupid wonderment.'

That places the origins of *le jardin anglais*, with its grass, woods and streams, fairly on the English.

Riat also cites the French translation of Thomson's *Seasons* (1730), and, inevitably, Rousseau's *La Nouvelle Héloise* (1761) with its celebrated description of Julia's secret garden at Clarens:

'After having admired the good consequences attending the vigilance and care of the prudent Julia in the conduct of her family, I was witness of the good effects of the recreation she uses in a retired place, where she takes her favourite walk, and which she calls her Elysium. . . .

'This place, though just close to the house, is so concealed by a shady walk, that it is not visible from any point. The thick foliage with which it is environed, renders it impervious to the eye, and it is always carefully locked up. I was scarce got within-side, but, the door being covered with alder and hazel trees, I could not find out which way I came in, when I turned back; and seeing no door, it seemed as if I had dropped from the clouds.

'Upon entering into this disguised orchard, I was seized with an agreeable sensation; the freshness of the thick foliage, the beautiful and lovely verdure, the flowers scattered on each side, the murmuring of the purling stream, and the warbling of a thousand birds, struck my imagination as powerfully as my senses; but at the same time I thought myself in the most wild and solitary place in nature, and I appeared as if I had been the first mortal who had ever penetrated into this desert spot. Being seized with astonishment, and transported at so unexpected a sight, I remained motionless for some time, and cried out, in an involuntary fit of enthu-

53. Bodnant, Denbigh-
shire.

54. Hergest Croft,
Herefordshire.

55. Benmore, Argyll.

56. Rowallane, Co. Down.

siasm, "O Tinian! O Juan Fernandez![1] Julia, the world's end is at your threshold!"

' "Many people," said she, with a smile, " think in the same manner; but twenty paces at most presently brings them back to Clarens: let us see whether the charm will work longer upon you. This is the same orchard where you have walked formerly, and where you have played at romps with my cousin. You may remember that the grass was almost burned up, the trees thinly planted, according very little shade, and that there was no water. You find that now it is fresh, verdant, cultivated, embellished with flowers, and well watered. What do you imagine it may have cost me to put into the condition you see? For you must know that I am the superintendent, and that my husband leaves the entire management of it to me."

' "In truth," said I, "it has cost you nothing but inattention. It is indeed a delightful spot, but wild and rustic; and I can discover no marks of human industry. . . ."

'I began to wander over the orchard thus metamorphosed with a kind of ecstasy; and if I found no exotic plants, nor any of the products of the Indies, I found all those that were natural to the soil, disposed and blended in such a manner as to produce the most cheerful and lively effect. The verdant turf thick, but shorn and close, was intermixed with wild thyme, balm, sweet marjoram, and other fragrant flowers. You might perceive a thousand wild flowers dazzle your eyes, among which you would be surprised to discover some garden-flowers, which seemed to grow natural with the rest. . . .'

And so on, round the serpentine walks, under trees garlanded with creepers and ingeniously planted epiphytes, and besides a clear and limpid rivulet (contrived from the stream that formerly fed the fountains) they wander.

It is surely all an emotional elaboration of Addison's *Spectator* essays of 1710 and 1712, and even a foreshadowing of William Robinson in the eighteen-eighties.

Riat also refers to works of the period on Greek ruins; Gerardin's *Composition des paysages* (1777); and the Abbé Delille's *Jardins* (1782). He does not here refer to the French translation of Walpole's *Essay on Modern Gardening* in 1785, or to the Prince de Ligne's *Coup d'Oeil sur Beloeil et sur un grand partie des jardins de l'Europe* (1781), which has much about the English landscape gardens that he visited, often critical.

It is not surprising that with these literary interventions, travellers

[1] Desert islands in the South Seas, celebrated in Lord Anson's voyage.

should find that the English gardens in Europe differed somewhat from their origins. From their descriptions and contemporary engravings all had, however, as one of their main elements, the irregular planting of trees, of grassy glades with streams within them, and curving pools.

And, when it came to making them, as often as not Britons (not infrequently Scots) were called in to do the job, usually having to struggle with the native designers to get their own way. The best known is Thomas Blaikie (1750–1838). He went to France in 1776, worked for the Comte de Lauragais, and later with the designer François Belanger and for the Duc d'Orleans. He was therefore ultimately concerned with such famous gardens as Bagatelle and Monceau. We know something of Blaikie's work – and his generally low opinion of the French garden designers – from his diary which has survived. He names other Englishmen and Scots working in France.

There were political and economic reasons for the spread of the English movement to Russia.

In 1762 the nobility no longer were compelled to attend the Court, and consequently some, at least, spent more time on their country estates. In 1785 a charter of the nobility was enacted demanding that they should improve the rural economy. This, in addition to the erection of farmsteads and factories, caused the creation of many parks embellished with ornamental buildings.

Andrei Bolotov (1738–1833) edited during the 1780s an influential agricultural journal which among other subjects dealt, as a matter of policy, with the development of parks. He laid down the principle that a park should be a naturally beautiful garden.

A prominent designer was Nikolai L'vov, an architect, engineer, poet and musician. As an architect, he worked in the Palladian style. As a gardener, he believed in the picturesque manner, but unlike some of its continental exponents, he was essentially practical and it is said that his roads and paths always had a purpose. His numerous buildings were beautifully designed. He produced antique sculpture in cast iron and delightful bridges in both the classical and gothic manners. The work of L'vov and other park designers has been described by Prof. M. Kjin.

A dominating figure was inevitably the anglophile Catherine II, who in 1772 wrote to Voltaire:

'I passionately love gardens in the English style, the curved lines, the gentle slopes, the ponds pretending to be lakes, the archipelagos on solid ground, and I deeply disdain straight lines. I hate fountains which torture the water by letting it flow along paths contrary to its nature; I should say that my anglomania gets the better of my planimetry.'

The Gardener's Magazine[1] of 1827 carries an account by 'One of the Imperial Gardeners' at the Russian Court of the introduction of the modern style to Russia, which, he tells us, was at the palace of Tsarskoe Selo. This had been built at extravagant cost by the Empress Elizabeth during her reign from 1714 to 1761. In this, the Dutch style of gardening prevailed, straight walks lined with trees all clipped in different forms.

Elizabeth was succeeded by Catherine II. In about 1768 she read Baron von Münchhausen's[2] *Hausvater*, 'which seemed to give Catherine a taste for modern gardening. She immediately ordered that no trees should be clipped in any of the imperial gardens, but that they should be left to nature. After this she told her architect and gardener, that in making gardens they should endeavour to follow nature; but this they could neither feel nor comprehend; they attempted to vary the straight line, by planting single trees on each side of the serpentine walks. This did not please; for though the Empress could not exactly indicate what they ought to do, yet she felt convinced in her own mind, that what they had done was not right. At a small distance from the garden there was a brook, of which the water meandered in a very pleasing style; before she left the country residence, which was about the first of September, she ordered a walk to be made on the side of the brook. This was completed, and in the spring of the year she went to see what had been done, and found they had made a walk on the side of the brook, but had kept it parallel with the bank, and had planted single trees at equal distances on each side of the walk. On her coming up to it she said, "No this will not do; this is not what I wanted." '

She determined to have an English gardener, though in the end it was a German, John Busch, whom she employed, for the reason that she could speak his language. Busch, however, had settled in England and was a

---

[1] At this period articles from this paper and *The Encyclopaedia of Gardening* (various editions), both edited by J. C. Loudon, provide useful information, for, with a knowledge both of the English style of gardening and of horticulture, he travelled widely over Europe between 1812 and 1820, going as far afield as Moscow, and recording his experiences in detail. He also quotes and makes great use of the voluminous writings of the Dane, Charles Caius Hirschfield, whose five-volumed *Theory of the Art of Gardening* (Leipsic, 1779–1785) has not been within my purview.

[2] He had laid out his English style garden at Schobbers, near Hameln, in 1750.

prominent nurseryman at Hackney.[1] In 1772 he began work, not at Tsarskoe, but a few miles away. She first saw what he had achieved in 1774. 'On entering the garden, and seeing a shady gravel walk, which was planted on each side and winding, she appeared struck with surprise, and said, "This is what I wanted." This walk led to a fine lawn, with gravel walks round it, which seemed to strike her still more forcibly, and she again said, "This is what I long wished to have." ' Busch duly took charge of the Tsarskoe gardens, returning to England in 1789, leaving his son John in charge.

Another enthusiast for the English manner was Prince Potemkin, who in 1780 began the palace and garden at Taurida. The garden was planned and managed by William Gould of Manchester, said by Loudon to have been a pupil of Brown. On a level site he dug ponds, out of which he obtained sufficient material to make 'an agreeable variety of swells and declivities'.

The most remarkable story of Potemkin's *anglomanie* was confirmed by Loudon from Call[2] – presumably another Englishman – when he was in Russia during 1813.

'In one of the Prince's journeys to the Ukraine, Gould attended him with several hundred assistants, designed for operators, in laying out the grounds of Potemkin's residence in the Crimea. Wherever the Prince halted, if only for a day, his travelling pavilion was erected, and surrounded by a garden in the English taste, composed of trees and shrubs, divided by gravel walks, and ornamented with seats and statues, all carried forward with the cavalcade. On another occasion, having accidentally discovered the ruins of a castle of Charles XII of Sweden, he immediately not only caused it to be repaired, but surrounded by gardens in the English taste.'

The famous garden designed in a highly formal manner by le Blond at Peterhof had an English garden added to it. It was designed and superintended by James Meader, formerly gardener to the Duke of Northumberland, apparently both at Alnwick and Syon, and author of a small book, *The Planter's Guide*. Letters that he wrote home between 1779 and 1787 have survived and been published by E. H. M. Cox. From them we learn that the so-called 'small' garden he was to make in the English style

---

[1] The business was acquired by a Dutchman, Conrad Loddiges, who, with his family, made it one of the most important nurseries in England.

[2] Possibly this man was 'the Imperial Gardener' who wrote in *The Gardener's Magazine*. The article is in faultless colloquial English. By 1827 Taurida Palace had passed to the Crown.

was a park full of fine trees, pieces of water, and a vale in which he hoped to form a cascade. The estate was bounded 'only by the Gulf of Finland'. His labour force was of 300 men. One of his difficulties was to obtain from Derbyshire adequate quantities of spar of the right kind to make a grotto like that at Painshill.

Though these expatriate gardeners were engaged principally as landscapers, their letters show that generally, except in France, they far excelled the natives as horticulturists. They built greenhouses, making fruit gardens and greatly improving the standards of routine gardening. Indeed, they seem to have been in short supply.

Again from Loudon we learn that English gardening was introduced into Poland by the Princess Isabella Czartoryska at Pulhawa. This highly accomplished lady of good taste and much sense spent a considerable time in England. 'She carried back to Poland a gardener Savage' and with him and the assistance of two local architects laid out her gardens in woodlands on the bank of the Vistula between 1780 and 1784, publishing in 1801 an illustrated work on English gardening.

The Austro-Hungarian nobility were conservative and clung to the French style, but the English manner eventually crept in. Robert Townson wrote in his *Travels in Hungary . . . in the year 1793* (without disguising his contempt for the old manner) of his visit to the gardens of Count Esterhazy near Doti, 'a great ornament of which is an unusual profusion of copious springs, of which they have availed themselves, not to form little piddling Cupids and puking ducks, but lakes and canals overhung by weeping willows, and limpid murmuring streams, on whose banks one would willingly repose, when inclined to meditate . . . or to pass some sweet moments with a tender female friend'. Later, near Tyrnau, he called on Count Erödy. 'He invited me to spend the day with him, and conducted me about his grounds, which he is only beginning to put in order, and they are to be *à L'Anglaise*: there is great *capability*.'

Loudon mentions, but does not name, Britons who worked in the German states. He also refers to German gardeners who visited England to study. Surprisingly, he does not say anything of Baron Caspar von Voght who, between 1793 and 1797, laid out the Jenisch-Park after visiting the Leasowes. He engaged a Scottish gardener, James Booth, who was later to form the famous Flottbek tree and shrub nurseries of James Booth and Sons whose 1838 catalogue he reprints in his *Arboretum et Fruticetum Brittannicum*.

We have already referred to Loudon's comments of 1819 on the English garden in Italy. The later editions of his *Encyclopaedia* enlarge on their history: 'About the middle of the eighteenth century, the English style of gardening began to attract attention in Italy; though, partly from the general stagnation of mind, and partly from the abundance of natural beauty already existing, it has never made much progress in that country.' He adds that the first natural or English gardens, using introduced trees and shrubs, were those laid out by the brothers Pecinardi near Cremona.

An early English garden in Italy was that laid out on the advice of Sir William Hamilton, the ambassador, in the 1780s at Caserta. Of this great palace with its now world-famed gardens, the Rev. J. Eustace wrote in his *Classical Tour Through Italy* in 1813, 'the gardens, extensive, regular, but except a part in the English style, uninteresting'. Loudon, too, was pleased with that part of the place (true, in 1819, the whole 'was much out of repair'). He wrote: 'The English garden of Caserta is as perfect a specimen of English pleasure-ground as any we have seen on the Continent. The verdure of the turf is maintained in summer by a partially concealed system of irrigation: and part of the walks was originally laid out with Kensington gravel. Every exotic which at that time could be furnished by the Hammersmith Nursery,[1] was planted; and many of them formed, when we saw them in 1819, very fine specimens. Among these the camellias, banksias, proteas, magnolias, pines, etc., had attained a large size and ripened their seeds.'

A Scottish landscape painter, Jacob More (1740–93) ('of Rome'), landscaped the park of the Villa Borghese.

The principal writer on and exponent of the English style in Italy was Count Ercole Silva, who, after visiting England and studying the English authors, published *Dell'arte de giardini inglesi* in 1801. He was, Hugh Honour observes, a great admirer of our crumbling abbeys, which could not be matched in Italy, and had an enthusiasm for flowers of which our earlier purists would not have approved. Silva may have been responsible for the English garden at Monza, whose grotto and island Loudon thought worthy of illustration.

As one considers the spread of the English style of garden throughout

---

[1] The Hammersmith Nursery (now buried under Olympia) was of international importance during the late eighteenth and early nineteenth centuries. James Lee (1715–1719) was in partnership there with Lewis Kennedy, and seems to have been the driving force. The nursery supplied to and obtained from the Continent a great variety of plants. Lewis Kennedy's grandson, another Lewis (1789–1877), was a garden designer of ability who worked at Wanstead, Trent Park, Oddington, and Woolmers in Hertfordshire where he was responsible for a parterre-style flower garden.

Europe, one cannot be thankful enough that so often it was no more than a complementary part or addition to an old garden, or else an entirely new undertaking. There was no continental Brown or Repton to let loose his vandalism on the old established manner.

Yet, there is one recurrent theme that runs through all the observations, even those that are critical, on the English manner of gardening, in whichever country it may be: it is the pleasure of seeing trees untortured, unregimented.

It was in North America that the English style was to become most firmly established and developed, yet when David Douglas visited the eastern states of the U.S.A. in 1823 ornamental gardening did not impress him. On visiting the garden of Mr Van Ransaleer of Albany, he wrote that he found that gentleman had 'a large space of ground occupied as a pleasure or flower garden, which is a novelty in America, as little attention is paid to anything but what brings money or luxury for the table'. A letter from Mr Jesse Buell in *The Gardener's Magazine* of 1828 stated that 'horticulture received but little attention in the United States, until quite a recent period; and with occasional exceptions, was limited to the culture of common culinary vegetables and fruits. A young people must earn the means of procuring the luxuries and elegances of horticultural refinement, before they can enjoy them. The wants and necessities of a new country are generally too imperious to leave much time, or to afford adequate means, for indulging extensively in the ornamental and scientific departments of gardening; and perhaps the republican principles of the government, and the habits of the people, have in a measure tended to retard improvement in these higher branches. Most men are ambitious of popular favour: and here, where all are on a political equity, whatever savours of singular ostentation or extravagance begets bad rather than good feelings. . . . Respectable gardens are occasionally found in the neighbourhood of large towns, but their number is too small, and the access to them too limited, to produce much influence towards general improvement.'

Perhaps Mr Buell was a little gloomy and not apparently aware of the enthusiastic Bartrams, nor the activities of President Jefferson, whose *Garden Book* records his gardening activities from 1766 to 1824. Then there are documented accounts of a number of eighteenth- and early nineteenth-century formal gardens in Georgia and Virginia.

The vogue of the English landscape garden was, however, very late in crossing the Atlantic. Its first great practitioner was Andrew Jackson

Downing (1815–52) of New York. In 1841 he published *A Treatise on the Theory and Practice of Landscape Gardening adapted to North America*. There is no doubt as to the origins of his ideas and methods. He wrote:

'The most distinguished English landscape gardeners of recent date are the late Humphry Repton, who died in 1818, and since him, John Claudius Loudon, better known in this country as the celebrated gardening author. Repton's taste in Landscape Gardening was cultivated and elegant, and many of the finest parks and pleasure grounds of England at the present day bear witness to the skill and harmony of his designs. His published works are full of instructive hints, and at Cobham Hall, one of the finest seats in Britain, is an inscription to his memory, by Lord Darnley.

'Mr Loudon's writings and labours in tasteful gardening are too well known to render it necessary that we should do more than allude to them here. Much of what is known of the art in this country undoubtedly is more or less directly to be referred to the influence of his published works. Although he is, as it seems to us, somewhat deficient as an artist in imagination, no previous author ever deduced, so clearly, sound artistical principles in Landscape Gardening and Rural Architecture; and fitness, good sense, and beauty, are combined with much unity of feeling in all his works.

'As the modern style owes its origin mainly to the English, so it has also been developed and carried to its greatest perfection in the British Islands...'

Downing was, indeed, something of the same type of man as Loudon, publishing, in 1850, *Architecture of Country Houses* with numerous delightful plates.

There is an absence of the egalitarianism of Mr Buell in his theories:

'This embellishment of nature, which we call Landscape Gardening, springs naturally from a love of country life, an attachment to a certain spot, and a desire to render that place attractive – a feeling which seems more or less strongly fixed in the minds of all men. But we should convey a false impression, were we to state that it may be applied with equal success to residences of every class and size, in the country. Lawn and trees, being its two essential elements, some of the beauties of Landscape Gardening may, indeed, be shown wherever a rood of grass surface and half a dozen trees are within our reach; we may, even with such scanty space, have tasteful grouping, varied surface, and agreeably curved walks; but our art, to appear to advantage, requires some extent of surface – its lines should lose themselves indefinitely, and unite agreeably and gradually into those of the surrounding country.

'In the case of large landed estates, its capabilities may be displayed to their full extent, as from fifty to five hundred acres may be devoted to a park or pleasure grounds. Most of its beauty and all its charms, may, however, be enjoyed in ten or twenty acres, fortunately situated, and well treated, and Landscape Gardening, in America, combined and working harmony as it is with our fine scenery, is already beginning to give us results scarcely less beautiful than those produced by its finest effects abroad. The lovely villa residences of our noble river and lake margins, when well treated – even in a few acres of tasteful foreground – seem so entirely to appropriate the whole adjacent landscape and to mingle so sweetly in their outlines with the woods, the valleys and the shores around them, that the effects are often truly enchanting.'

Of the part played by trees:

'Among all the materials at our disposal for the embellishment of country residences, none are at once so highly ornamental, so indispensable, and so easily managed, as *trees*, or *wood*. We introduce them in every part of the landscape – in the foreground as well as in the distance, on the tops of the hills and in the depths of the valleys. . . .

'In the majority of instances in the United States, the modern style of landscape gardening, wherever it is appreciated, will, in practice, consist in arranging a demesne of from five to some hundred acres – or, rather that portion of it, say one half, one third, etc. devoted to lawn and pleasure ground, parterres, etc. – so as to exhibit groups of forest and ornamental trees and shrubs, surrounding the dwelling of the proprietor, and extending for a greater or less distance, especially towards the place of public entrance from the highway. Near the house, good taste will dictate the assemblage of groups and masses of the rarer or more beautiful trees and shrubs; commoner native forest trees occupying the more distant portions of the grounds.

'In the modern style of landscape gardening, it is our aim, in plantations, to produce not only what is called natural beauty, but even higher and more striking beauty of expression, and of individual forms, than we see in nature; to create variety and intricacy in the grounds of a residence by various modes of arrangement, to give a highly elegant or polished air to the places by introducing rare and foreign species; and to conceal all defects of surface, disagreeable views, unsightly buildings, or other offensive objects.'

He described a dozen or so landscaped estates.

Downing died when still a young man. His assistant had been Calvert

Vaux (1824–95), trained as an architect in England and taken to America by Downing in 1850, who carried on the same tradition, to be joined for a time with Frederick Law Olmstead (1822–1903) of Hartford, Connecticut. His visits to England and the lessons he learned by seeing Paxton's Reptonian essays, as, for example, Birkenhead Park and its circulatory road (which is mentioned later), were important influences. He was, it seems, the first to drop the title of landscape gardener and substitute landscape architect. He became prominent when he was appointed superintendent of Central Park, New York City, in 1857. After interruption caused by the Civil War, he developed his practice in a large way, training a number of younger men, including his son and stepson, who successfully carried on his theories. These have been summarised as follows, and remind us that he was working in a country where the scale was often vastly larger than the lands where the art of landscaping was evolved. His first objective was to retain the natural scenery, and if necessary to restore and emphasise its essential qualities. Then he would keep the open spaces within the centre of the area he was landscaping, using native trees and shrubs in heavily planted borders surrounding them; in this, as markedly distinct from European countries, he had a wealth of native material. (C. S. Sargent in his *Manual of the Trees of North America* describes nearly 800 kinds of trees, as distinct from shrubs – though some only grow in a restricted area.) Formal design he would not allow, except immediately surrounding buildings. A principal road circumscribed the whole area, with minor circulatory roads and paths laid out in wide, sweeping curves.

He was inevitably greatly concerned with trees and conserving wild life. An example of this type of his work is in the Bayard Cutting Arboretum, an area of 690 acres which is also a flower and nature reserve near the Great River, Long Island, begun as early as 1887. He was, indeed, one of the first landscapers to appreciate the great use that could be made of open spaces reserved for the public enjoyment and to bring into their planning the important element of transport to and within them of the rapidly increasing urban population.

CHAPTER EIGHT

The Nineteenth Century

MISGUIDED EFFORT

TO US, who live in the twentieth century with its all-embracing wars, it is amazing that the battle of the picturesque, and the planned alterations for purely aesthetic purposes of thousands of acres of the British countryside, took place against a background of international warfare in which we were usually deeply involved.

Surprisingly, it was the outbreak of the French Revolutionary Wars that delayed the implementation of the Commissioners' suggestions; meanwhile, for a period our timber shortages were increased by the French blockade of the Baltic ports, which interfered with our now considerable imports of 'fir', or softwoods. Further, the supplies of native timber for the Navy were, as is usual in times of shortage, controlled by middlemen using elaborate methods of corruption.

No action was taken to plant in the Royal Forests until after 1803, when Lord Glenbervie was appointed Surveyor General of Woods and Forests. On 5th December, 1804, Lord Dundas, First Lord of the Admiralty, wrote to him raising still once more the serious deficiency of naval oak, adding that were it a matter of famine or pestilence, everyone would be alive to the danger. At that time, the only timber enclosures in the Royal Forests were 676 acres in Dean and 1207 acres in the New Forest – even so, the fencing and general condition were in a state of neglect.

Glenbervie tackled the shortage energetically; in 1810 he was appointed first chief commissioner of the new united land and forest board, and in 1814 was succeeded by William Huskisson, who remained (much against his inclination) chief commissioner until 1823. About the time he assumed office, he compiled a memorandum in which he reported that Glenbervie had enclosed and drained 40,000 acres, and begun planting. All work, except planting, was done under contract by open competition. The era of restocking really began in 1808, with 1,776 acres completed, until in 1849 33,000 acres had been planted.

Henceforth, the timber-producing areas of the Royal Forests were well managed – with a view to obtaining, in a century or more, massive, open-grown oak, gnarled and crooked, for the type of ship that had fought under Nelson. However, by then our 'wooden walls' had long ceased to be 'the best walls of this kingdom'. It is unfortunate that these highly artificial oakwoods, so unlike the natural woodland, still remain in the mind of a large part of the public as the idealised image of our natural forests (Plate 40).

In the meantime, as the saplings grew up, from about 1817 and for another thirty years, the supply of naval timber was virtually controlled by a certain master of corruption named John Morris, or Morrice – a shadowy figure of whom (not surprisingly) little seems known.

And, even while Morris carried on his nefarious operations, iron and steel were steadily replacing our oak, while imports of cheaper timber from those countries with huge, almost untouched natural resources – the Scandinavian countries, Russia and North America – steadily increased. From 1843 to 1882 these imports of softwoods trebled, from 90 to 290 million cubic feet. As early as 1823, William Cobbett, having seen the false acacia (*Robinia pseudacacia*) used in North America for boat building, and with us a very quick-growing tree (it had been introduced here, and its speed of growth noted, by 1640), started a campaign to plant it in our forests; he had himself astutely acquired a large stock of seedlings for sale.

Many books on the production of timber trees in all its aspects were published. Although the importance today of the greatest of all, Loudon's *Arboretum et Fruticetum Britannicum* (1838), seems largely arboricultural, it was the first of exhaustive, scientifically based studies of the management of our timber producing trees – again, with the shipbuilding element much to the fore. Even as late as 1851, the year of the Great Exhibition, an able and exhaustive practical work such as James Nisbet's *The Forester* cites as an example of the economic value and importance of forestry that a seventy-four gun ship requires 'no less than the matured crop of forty-four acres of woodland, or two thousand, two hundred full-grown trees',[1] and that the natural forests abroad are unlikely to supply the great and increasing demands of the British Navy.

---

[1] In my copy, this passage is heavily underlined. The interest in the then modern methods of forestry was so great that the first edition of 1847 had been sold out.

Probably planting was carried out most extensively in Scotland, particularly in the far north. For example, the *Transactions of the Highland and Agricultural Society of Scotland* for 1837 reports plantations on an extensive scale, principally of Scots pine and larch, over the preceding years as far north as Skibo, Sutherland and Kilcoy, Rosshire. At Strathdon in West Aberdeenshire, there was very considerable planting, again of Scots pine and larch, between 1800 and 1830, with a slower rate continuing to 1870. The total was some 4,000 acres, against the 1965 goal of 9,000 acres: an important and interesting comparison.

In general, in Victorian times, our forests made none of the spectacular progress as did the industries based on coal and iron. Industry, in its turn, had long ceased to make demands on our forests for fuel.

Home-grown timber was used for farm and estate work, for wagon and coach building, and a multitude of rural crafts – all so interestingly described in George Sturt's *Wheelright's Shop* – carried out with the most elementary machinery by highly skilled (and highly respected) craftsmen. Tanning and charcoal burning carried on as important local undertakings until well into the next century. Oakwoods were regularly coppiced for this purpose, with the result that as the industries died out the stools grew up to provide the great areas of rough, valueless timber that we now possess – in many cases bearing no resemblance to the fine naval timber that was intended. In the hop-growing areas, chestnut poles were valuable for the 'wire-work'.

The woodlands on many great estates were not economically worth felling, and were maintained to give pleasure and for sport; our love of sport has been the means of saving much magnificent woodland. Fortune-making industrialists, with no knowledge of forestry, or, for that matter, country life, bought wooded estates to provide sport for their friends.

The traditions of good forestry, and a belief, or rather hope, in its future, were, however, continuously held by a number of landowners, although – possibly fostered by astute publicity by the now large financial interests concerned in the import of foreign wood – a body of prejudice was built up against home-grown timber.

And there was something in this. The timber that was now beginning to mature had been planted for shipbuilding and not for the many and rapidly increasing requirements of the industrial age. Yet once again our national foresight was noticeably absent. We were in a period of peace and the possibility that our island position might again be vulnerable even to desperation was not considered. To quote Stebbing, '. . . the abolition of the import duties on Colonial timber in 1846, and for all other foreign timber in 1866, sounded the death-knell of British forestry methods as at that time practised'. And there was no incentive to plant timber to meet the changed needs of the next century on the spacious agriculturally infertile areas that would support it.

Scotland, as has been made clear, had for a century and more been ahead with afforestation – so much of its land being best suited to growing timber trees. The Highland and Agricultural Society of Scotland had long given support to these activities. In 1854 was formed the Scottish Arboricultural Society (to become the Royal Scottish Forestry Society). South of the Border, at a meeting at Hexham in 1882, was formed the English Arbori-cultural Society (now the Royal Forestry Society of England, Wales and Northern Ireland). The term arboriculture in those days had a much wider meaning than it now has; indeed, a dictionary meaning today is still 'the cultivation of trees and shrubs, forestry'. Arboriculture has now become associated with the cultivation of ornamental trees, while forestry has become the production in forests (another word that has, with the exception of 'deer-forests', entirely changed its original meaning) of trees for the manifold economic uses of their wood and all relating thereto, silviculture having become reserved for the actual cultivation of trees. It should be added that both societies, though their principal concern is with forestry, have con-tinuously taken a great interest in arboriculture. It can, in fact, be said without hesitation that modern forestry has arisen, and is still drawing inspiration, from the arboriculturist, that class of 'curious' – in the eighteenth-century sense – persons which grows trees primarily as a matter of interest and pleasure.

These two bodies, often working behind the scenes, have had a singular effect on our woodlands and countryside. At a time when great areas of our woodlands were in a state of neglect, often no more than sporting preserves, they foresaw that a time might come, as it did, when we should be desperately short of timber; they foresaw the need for the introduction of scientific methods into forestry, and scientific training of its operatives. Once again, as in the days when the Royal Society of Arts awarded prizes for planting, it was a small body of private individuals that acted while governments and civil servants drifted incompetently along.

THE VICTORIAN CONIFERS

Probably the public no longer associates the giant conifers which are now the staple of much forestry – not only in the British Isles but in many parts of the world – with the age of Queen Victoria. In fact, the history of their introduction – an epoch-making period in the story of our landscape – begins a few decades before she came to the throne. But it was during her reign that they became widely known and were typical inmates, and at first novelties, in the gardens of the great and to some extent in woodlands.

Between 1790 and 1795 Captain George Vancouver bullied his crew into making one of the most important voyages of discovery recorded, taking in the Cape, New Zealand and North-west America. One of the crew who suffered him was a Scot, Archibald Menzies, the surgeon and botanist on the voyage. Menzies is well enough known as the introducer of the Chilean monkey-puzzle (*Araucaria araucana*), of which he brought back seedlings sown and germinated on the voyage.[1] On the Pacific coast of North America he was among the first to record and describe a number of trees that were to change the landscape of the British Isles. In 1791 he discovered the Douglas fir (*Pseudotsuga menziesii* or *taxifolia*), in 1792 the Sitka spruce (*Picea sitchensis*), in 1793 the Nootka cypress (*Chamaecyparis nootkatensis*) and in 1795 he rediscovered the giant redwood (*Sequoia sempervirens*), which had earlier been known to the Spanish.

None of these did he introduce. The Horticultural Society of London (later to become the Royal Horticultural Society) was formed at a meeting at Hatchard's bookshop in Piccadilly in March, 1804, and soon became active in introducing new plants from abroad. They were naturally interested in the rich flora of the then virtually unexplored Pacific coast of North America, not only on account of what Menzies had described, but from the discoveries of overland expeditions such as that of Lewis and Clarke.

In 1823 they engaged a young Scot, David Douglas (1799–1834), to collect seeds of plants in this strange new world. After a preliminary trip to the eastern states, he sailed in July, 1824, to the west. No other collector excelled Douglas in the importance of his introductions, and but for his early death he would no doubt have introduced much that was left for his successors, the most important of whom was William Lobb (1809–63). The kinds collected by Douglas were in short supply just at the time it became the vogue to grow them. The enterprising Veitch family of nurserymen at Exeter realised that 'young plants of most of the important species could

[1] The delightful story that Menzies pocketed the seeds served at a banquet unfortunately cannot be true. Uncooked seeds are inedible. Today, the natives still go out and collect sacks-full off the ground for eating; they are boiled and are then like sweet chestnuts.

scarcely be bought with money'. They decided that to obtain large quantities of seed would be a profitable enterprise, and they chose Lobb, who already worked for them, to be their collector. His first visit, from 1840 to 1844, was to South America, whence he brought orchids (also becoming very fashionable) and a number of trees and shrubs, mostly not very hardy. The one exception was the monkey-puzzle, which was extremely rare owing to difficulties of collection. Lobb obtained lots of seed and Veitch launched this tree on its, literally, spectacular career. In 1849 Lobb arrived in San Francisco to follow up where Douglas left off. He collected further large quantities of seeds of Douglas's introductions, achieving a spectacular success in 1853 when he sent home the first specimens and much seed of the wellingtonia (*Sequoiadendron giganteum*) and the western arbor-vitae (*Thuja plicata*). The first became as fashionable as the monkey-puzzle, while the second is now a tree of considerable economic importance. Lobb came back to England with these trophies in 1853, returning to California, where he lived until his death in 1864.

The rapid growth of these Californian conifers, and their potential as fast producers of timber, particularly in the western and south-western parts of our islands, their handsome form and foliage, and the inevitable cult of the new, caused many landowners to become enthusiastic in their planting. In 1849 a meeting was called at the Royal Botanic Garden, Edinburgh, which in 1850 formed 'an association of noblemen and gentlemen, chiefly Scotch, for the purpose of promoting the botanical exploration of north-west America, and the introduction into Great Britain of plants and trees, especially Coniferae, indigenous to that region'. The organisation was called the Oregon Association, with the Prince Consort as patron.

The moving spirit was George Patton, later Lord Glenalmond (1803–69), a Scottish judge. Professor J. H. Balfour was chairman. In 1850 John Jeffrey (1826–c. 1853) was engaged as collector and went overseas. He began admirably and sent valuable collections of seed of some thirty trees which were raised by the members. By 1853 his activities had become negligible, and he disappeared without trace. However, he had done good work, and several introductions of interesting, but only one commercially important tree – the lodgepole pine – stand to his credit, apart from his useful reintroductions of earlier discoveries.

The Victorian conifers also include other purely ornamental trees – western American, African and Asian – which now play their part in the landscape; these will be mentioned later. In the meantime, one may look

57. Eastwoodhill,
Gisborne, New
Zealand.

58. Green returns
to the valley;
Ebbw Vale,
Monmouthshire.

59. Lake Vyrnwy, Montgomeryshire, in winter.

60. The new landscape, England: Kielder, Northumberland.

at the receiving end. The enthusiasm for pineta – in reality a collection of conifers, not restricted to pines – began in the late eighteenth century. The first major work in English relating to conifers was *The Genus Pinus* by Aylmer Bourke Lambert (1761–1842) of Boyton in Wiltshire. Again, the title is misleading as in the early days this genus included several others not now included in it. The first two huge volumes appeared in 1803, illustrated by Ferdinand Bauer and James Sowerby. They formed an exhaustive study of the conifers then known. Some Lambert grew himself, other living specimens he obtained from Painshill, presumably planted by Hamilton before he sold the place in 1775.[1] Another source was Orford Hall, near Warrington in Lancashire, where a collection was made by John Blackburne (1690–1786) and his daughter Anne (1740–93). Even by that time, a considerable number of conifers had been introduced from Europe, Asia and the eastern states of North America. Lambert lived to see and describe Douglas's introductions. The sugar pine, with its cones a foot or more long, discovered by Douglas in 1825, was named *Pinus lambertiana*; in a letter to a friend he wrote of this monster[2]: 'What would Dr Hooker do to dine under its shade, Mr Lambert could not eat anything if he saw it.'

It is interesting to summarise a detailed description of the important pineta where these conifers were first received and cultivated, given in *The Gardener's Magazine* for 1838. There were listed sixty-nine species in all. Their presence or otherwise, together with height where available, was noted at the following collections, the date of establishment being given in brackets:

Kew, Surrey (1760), Dropmore, Berkshire (1796), Hackney – the nursery of Conrad Loddiges and Sons (1819), Horticultural Society's Gardens at Chiswick (1823), Belsay, Northumberland (1825), Flitwick, Bedfordshire (1826), Cheshunt, Hertfordshire (1830), Chatsworth, Derbyshire (1835), Carclew, Cornwall (1835), Chipstead, Kent (1835), Hendon Rectory, Middlesex (1836), Woburn Abbey, Bedfordshire (1836), Elvaston Castle, Derbyshire (1834), Royal Botanic Garden, Edinburgh (1825), Lahill, Fifeshire (1830), Haddo House, Aberdeenshire (1834), Ballindalloch, Inverness-shire (1834), and Glasnevin Botanical Garden, Dublin (1797).

[1] In about 1781 Sir Joseph Banks took there Charles von Linné (the son of the great Linnaeus), who stated that it contained a greater variety of firs (conifers) than any other place in the world that he had visited.

[2] It is one of the five-needled pines that in this country seldom reach any great size as they are attacked by a pine 'rust'. Lambert's pine is also a shy seeder.

There are certain other early pineta still in existence, such as Bicton, Devonshire, laid out in 1830. Dropmore is of great interest, as its development has been almost unbroken, and, over the years it has existed, much has been both recorded and published about the trees. The dates of planting of a number of specimens is known. Between 1796 and his death in 1834 Lord Grenville, whose gardeners made the first plantings of trees from seed obtained from New York, received shares in the Horticultural Society's collections. There are still some survivors of their early plantings in the collection.

Of the trees these great and enterprising landowners grew, the first in importance today is Sitka spruce, which has been planted in large numbers in those parts of the British Isles where it will thrive, which happen to be the wetter, wilder and otherwise infertile places. An American writer has described it: 'The black-looking wind-blown tree along the shore-line. . . . The strong west wind off the ocean streams upward with the slope of the Coast Range, and shapes the crown of this tree exactly in line with that flow. It is actually rigid and resistant, but in appearance like a torn banner flapping in the wind. . . . The blackness of the tree in the contrast of its silhouette against bright seascapes.'

It is the largest and heaviest of the eighteen American spruces, growing in the coastal belt from Alaska to California, sometimes climbing 3,000 feet up the mountains. At the northernmost end of its range it is little more than a bush, but under conditions that suit it, 280 feet has been exceeded. A tree in Alaska was found aged 764 years.

Menzies first collected it in May, 1792. Douglas sent home seed in 1831, but Menzies' spruce, as it was first called, remained rare until Jeffreys sent the Oregon Association a large quantity in 1852.

It was, of course, first grown here as a specimen tree, particularly, as might be expected, in Scotland. An early plantation was that at Wooplaw, Roxburghshire, in 1866.

The vigorous growth of many of these early plantings encouraged foresters during the end of the last and particularly the beginning of the present century to grow 'sitka' (to which the name is usually abbreviated) in increasing numbers. It was soon found that it does best where the rainfall is heavy, and that, because it will stand exposure, particularly to strong wind, it could be grown successfully at higher elevations than other trees. In our modern forests, therefore, sitka is now found quite abundantly in the forests of the Welsh and Scottish mountains. The timber they produce has a number of uses, though not strong structurally.

A height of 164 feet has been achieved in Perthshire, and a girth of over 24 feet in Devon. All who have to deal with this tree dislike the unpleasantly sharp-pointed leaves.

Douglas will be remembered with even more gratitude for the tree that bears his name. The Douglas fir (*Pseudotsuga menziesii*, formerly *taxifolia*) is a handsome tree, and its particular qualities are quick growth combined with a high ratio of strength to weight, and resistance to decay (Plate 41).

It is found over a wide area in north-west America, growing up in the Rocky Mountains, though the finest trees are found nearer sea-level. Discovered by Menzies in Nootka Sound in 1797, Douglas sent home seed in 1827. One of those to sow them was David Frost at Dropmore, and there one of his trees may still be seen, now 118 feet high. In America, it is the next tallest tree to the redwood. In the British Isles, it is our tallest tree, reaching 181 feet or more at Powis Castle in Montgomeryshire. It also includes a far greater number of examples above 150 feet than any other kind. Thus, when grown among different species, as is not infrequent, its tall stature, with a flattened yet rather waving, deep green branch system, is a signal feature in the landscape.

The foliage, when crushed, is fragrant – like pineapples, some say – the buds pointed like a beech, the cone with prongs emerging from under the scales, and when old, a bark that may be dramatically furrowed.

This superb memorial to David Douglas[1] is one of the finest trees we have, with, in view of the great size it so often reaches, a surprising disadvantage: at certain stages of its growth, and in certain situations, it may easily be thrown over by the wind.

Another conifer introduced by Douglas is the Monterey pine (*Pinus radiata*, formerly *insignis*) which he sent in 1833 (Plate 42). This is not usual in our woodlands, but is of great importance in countries such as Australia, New Zealand and South Africa. The reason for this is that it is not hardy in many parts of the British Isles, but in a warmer climate grows at prodigious speed. In our milder counties, such as Cornwall, it often plays a considerable part in the landscape, for it will withstand the salty sea gales and makes a valuable wind-break. As such, it is of importance in many landscape gardens on our southern and western coasts. Elsewhere, in places that are not too cold, it is often seen in collections. It is a three-leaved pine – that is, the needles are in bundles of three – with large, knobbly cones that remain clustered round the leafless branches, unopened,

[1] Subsequently, both Jeffreys and Lobb sent home large quantities of seed.

for many years. The leaves are a rich grass-green, densely clustered on the shoots, which, with the broadly-rounded head, give it great distinction, contrasting with the pointed or spire-like form of so many conifers.

This tree, now so widely spread throughout the world, grows as a native only on and around a small area, the Monterey Peninsula. Douglas found it in 1831 and introduced it in 1832. In its wind-swept Californian home it seldom manages to reach any great size. In the more placid climate of Hampshire it has touched, and possibly exceeded, 180 feet. Also from this same limited wind-swept district, with its humid climate, comes the tree commonly known with us as 'macrocarpa', and found usually as a hedge. It is the Monterey cypress, *Cupressus macrocarpa*, easily distinguished from the Mediterranean cypress by its much larger cones and broad crown. This tree needs situations in this country comparable with the Monterey pine, and like it, is often seen at the seaside grown as wind-break. The timber is of no value. Douglas was not responsible for its introduction, and, so far as is known, A. B. Lambert obtained seeds from an unknown source in 1836, which he gave to the Horticultural Society. The first large introduction of seed was by Carl Hartweg in 1846, a German who collected for the Horticultural Society.

Two more discoveries and introductions by Douglas, fairly commonly planted for ornament, but now being used more and more in our forests, have acquired the vernacular names 'grandis' and 'nobilis', both being silver firs, or *Abies*,[1] with the botanical epithets *grandis*, meaning large, and *nobilis*, meaning 'stately'[2] – translations which are not particularly distinctive.

'Grandis' comes from a considerable area, where it is often common, on the coast from Vancouver down to California, at the middle of its range spreading far inland. The leaves are large and spread distinctively on either side of the twig in two flattened rows; when crushed they are aromatic. Douglas discovered the tree on the Columbia River in 1825, sending seed home in 1830, which produced only a few plants. As with so many of Douglas's introductions, the later reintroductions of Lobb and Jeffrey in larger quantities were much more successful. This conifer is hardy, probably the most rapid-growing and heaviest timber producer we have, though the wood is not of high quality. Planting in our forests

---

[1] The silver firs are so-called because they are roughly distinguished from the spruce firs (*Picea*) by the silver bands on their leaves.

[2] The correct botanical name is probably *A. procera*, meaning 'tall fir'.

greatly increased after the First World War. It has exceeded 160 feet in Argyll.

'Nobilis' is one of the most beautiful of Pacific conifers. An erect, rigid tree, not very densely branched, with little taper and a rounded top, the silvery undersides of the leaves give it a greyish colour, which, when planted among the more sombre evergreens, effectively lightens the mass. The leaves on the twigs are parted as if by a comb, and then swept back as if brushed. The massive cones – usually only in the treetops, where they are held rigidly erect until they crumble away – have spine-like growths emerging from under the scales. This justifies one name, feather-cone fir.

With a range from the north of Washington to mid-Oregon, it is essentially a mountain tree. Douglas discovered it on the south side of the Columbia River in 1825 and from him the Horticultural Society received seeds in 1831. The seedlings fetched fifteen to twenty guineas each, with the consequence that many trees were propagated by grafting and from cuttings. These did not grow well. It is said that the first crop of seed produced in this country was sold for forty pounds. It was realised that nobilis was hardy and did well in this country, and, following the timber shortage after the First World War, plantations were made. It is proving to be an excellent tree for our mountainous areas, where there is good rainfall. In Northern Ireland it succeeds where Scots pine is a failure. More and more is it likely, therefore, to enter our landscape, standing out, glaucous, among the more sombre greens.

For some unaccountable reason Douglas never introduced the most stupendous conifer of all, the Californian redwood (*Sequoia sempervirens*). Yet he knew of it, and wrote that it was the great beauty of Californian vegetation, giving 'the mountains a most peculiar, I was almost going to saw awful, appearance, something that plainly tells us we are not in Europe'.

This redwood is the tallest tree in the world. To stand in a grove in the British Isles – not much more than a century old – already gives that feeling of awe – or should one say of profound dignity and respect? – that Douglas felt (Plate 43). From the heavy boles, one looks up the great columns, with their shredded, glowing red bark, to the dense green canopy above, giving a sensation of deep shade, yet of spaciousness and height. The tallest tree ever measured was 364 feet high, which compares with 135 feet achieved in this country by 1962.

The Californian redwood is a tree of the coastal land, almost entirely restricted to a narrow belt in California, delighting in moisture and fog. It was observed by Spanish travellers in the eighteenth century. In 1795 Menzies collected specimens from which Lambert made the first description. Yet not until 1846 do we find any reference to the tree being grown in this country – a surprising fact in an age when conifers were so much the vogue, particularly as specimens of the foliage and cones had been brought here. The events of its introduction are surprising, and recall the ironic situation that at the beginning of the last century the Russians attempted to colonise California, but in 1841 abandoned their efforts as a failure after twenty-nine years. They had, however, sent home botanical specimens and plants. The consequence was that the redwood was introduced to England by means of plants sent by Dr Fischer, the Petersburg botanist, to Knight and Perry, nurserymen, of Chelsea. Also surprising at first sight was the fact that the value of the native timber was not realised until about 1840; this is explained, however, because the natives used adobe (mud) construction for their houses, not timber.

Many specimens of redwoods have, during and since the eighteen-forties, been planted in isolation or in small groups. The discovery that a forest plantation made at Leighton, Montgomeryshire, in about 1856 was producing timber (which in California is of considerable value) at a very heavy rate[1] has resulted in its use for forestry in those milder southern and western districts where it will thrive. It may well become an important and dramatic feature of the landscape. Unlike most conifers, the leaves often become scorched to a copper colour in severe winters without hurt to the tree.

If the tallest tree in the world slipped into our islands unheralded, the arrival of the biggest tree in the world was announced with almost twentieth-century publicity. The wellingtonia, for as such it is still known by the British, though of little commercial use, spires up as a landmark to signify the presence of many hundreds of aristocratic seats and gentlemen's residencies throughout the British Isles.

Sequoiadendron giganteum (it is related to *Sequoia*, from which it is at once distinguished by its pointed crown and cord-like shoots), while not so tall as the redwood, can carry a greater weight of timber than any other in the world – some probably weigh over a thousand tons (Plate 44). Trees still living were growing in the time of Christ, though the reputed ages of some other conifers, up to 4,000 years old are not disputed.

[1] At Dartington, South Devon, it has exceeded 60 feet in twenty years.
[2] In 1957 a living bristle-cone pine (*Pinus aristata*) 4,600 years old was found in

Both the redwood and wellingtonia are remnants of an ancient race which covered a great area as far north as the Arctic zone in Tertiary and Cretaceous times. The wellingtonia has a much more restricted range than the redwood, growing further inland, on higher and cooler sites out of the fog belt, where deep snow provides much of the moisture that the tree needs, and where temperatures may fall below zero. For this reason, there are few parts of the British Isles (free from industrial air pollution) where it will not stand erect and unharmed by gales or cold.

The first white man to discover a grove of these trees was John Bidwell in 1841. No one seems to have taken his claim seriously until a miner named Dowd out hunting came into the now famous Calaveros Grove. Back in camp, he was also disbelieved until, on another hunting expedition, he surreptitiously led his party to the trees. That was in 1852, and the fame of the tree spread rapidly. William Lobb had been collecting in California for the astute firm of Veitch since 1849. He heard all about the sensational discovery, and on his return to England in 1853 he brought with him specimens and a lot of seed.[1]

In the Christmas Eve issue of *The Gardener's Chronicle* of that year John Lindley, the editor, wrote:

'The other day we received from Mr Veitch branches and cones of a most remarkable coniferous tree . . . brought him by his excellent collector, Mr Lobb. . . . What a tree this is. The specimen felled at the junction of the Stanislau and San Antonio was above three thousand years old; that is to say, it must have been a little plant when Samson was slaying the Philistines, or Paris running away with Helen. . . . No one will differ from us in feeling that the most appropriate name to be proposed for the most gigantic tree which has been revealed to us by modern discovery is that of the greatest of modern heroes. Wellington stands as high above his contemporaries as the Californian tree above all the surrounding forest. Let it be given the name *Wellingtonia gigantea*.'

Unfortunately, the peculiarities followed by botanists in naming plants have outmoded Lindley's name – and only in the British Isles do we still connect the tree with the duke. For how long our singularly apt linking of two giants will survive is uncertain. Our country houses steadily disappear, and with them their trees. The wellingtonia has no value as timber, and no one now plants them. Like the mansions whose presence

California, which undoubtedly broke any claim of the wellingtonia to be the oldest tree in the world.

[1] Certainly one, and possibly two, small-scale introductions preceded Lobb's.

in the distant landscape is marked by these towering, yet discreet, exclamation marks, the wellingtonia will fade away. Even now, very few young trees are found. Most go back to the fifties, sixties and seventies of last century. One may recall the line 'tall oaks from little acorns grow' as Wellingtonias have minute flat, winged seeds, an eighth of an inch in length.

This is the place to mention that other astonishing Victorian, the monkey-puzzle (Plate 45), now classed inopportunely with other Victoriana such as the antimacassar; to Lobb, also, we owe this.

This sombre tree with its serpent-like, spiny-leaved branches was first reported by a Spanish traveller, Don Francisco Dendariarena in 1780, growing in the land of the Arauco tribe in western Chile – hence its botanical name *Araucaria araucana* (a botanically outmoded, but once generally used epithet was *imbricata*). In 1782 the botanist Pavon was sent to make a further report, and from the specimens he sent to France, de Jussieu botanically described and named it. The strange Chile pine, as it was called, caused great interest. A German traveller calculated that the seeds from eighteen trees would nourish a person for a year, though admitting that they upset his own stomach.

No one was sufficiently interested to bring live specimens to Europe until, as has been related, Menzies obtained seed from which he raised plants. These he gave to Sir Joseph Banks. One survived at Kew until 1892, having spent its early years cosseted in a greenhouse – the usual practice with introductions at that period (which incidentally killed off a good many hardy plants). In 1806 the curator, the famous Mr M'Nab, put it out of doors and triumphantly proved it to be hardy. A few early seedlings came into this country, probably imported via Holland. Apparently seed was difficult to purchase in Valparaiso, as it could only be obtained ready roasted.

In 1834 Sir William Molesworth of Pencarrow managed to buy a plant from Knight and Perry of Chelsea for, it is said, twenty-five pounds. The planting of such an expensive tree was the occasion of a solemn ceremony during a house-party. One of the guests was the distinguished barrister and conversationalist, Charles Austin. Incautiously grasping a branch, he casually remarked that it would puzzle a monkey to climb such a tree. So was born this unusual name, which must have helped to popularise the tree. The firm of Veitch, realising the commercial possibilities of this rare novelty, instructed their new collector William Lobb, who had been sent to South America, to obtain seeds. As a result, in 1843 the firm was able to offer 'many thousands . . . in quantity at a very low price'. (Ten pounds per hundred for seedlings four to six inches high.)

Thus began its career as an eccentric decoration of the British landscape. Like the wellingtonia, it will gradually disappear, for the type of situation that it so often ornaments is attaining a picturesque dereliction 'prior to development'. Economically, it has no value. Nor can it be fitted into a suburbia short of space and clean air.

Another of Lobb's introductions is fortunately beginning to find its way into our scenery as a tree of forest importance, as well as of beauty as an ornament. Variously known as *Thuja plicata*, western red cedar,[1] arbor-vitae, or now most commonly simply thuja – the 'j' usually pronounced as if it were a 'y' – it was first reported by the traveller Nees, who journeyed round the world with Malespina between 1789 and 1794, and who obtained specimens from Nootka Sound. Menzies also brought back specimens from the same place in 1795 (Plate 46).

Thuja grows over a wide area of western North America, from Alaska down to California, in the middle of this range well inland and up into the Rocky Mountains. It will therefore grow successfully in the British Isles over a wider area than the conifers that hug the Pacific coast. The tree is narrow and graceful in outline. The leaves are small and overlap on the twigs, which form a lace-like spray, of a bright, cheerful green. When crushed they have a distinctive, quite strong and most pleasant scent, so justifying the original meaning of cedar. The tree reaches no great size, and naturally grows not on its own, but in mixture with other trees. The wood, at present mostly imported, is well known for its use as shingles (wooden tiles) and for the exterior of wooden buildings. It withstands exposure, resisting moisture in winter and warping in summer. Stakes made from it last in the ground for many years. The native Indians used it for their totem poles and canoes.

Soon after its introduction, thuja became popular as an ornamental tree, and because it will stand clipping for hedges. Small experimental plots were grown in forests, but not until 1919 did planting on any scale begin. In the last decade this has increased considerably, though restricted somewhat by an epidemic fungal disease which attacks the small seedlings. Thuja is already playing a noticeable part in our forest landscape, which will increase.

Another of the western American conifers is Lawson's cypress, now

[1] Botanically, it is not a cedar; this is the now well-known name of the timber in commerce.

ubiquitous in its protean range of forms throughout our suburban parks and gardens. The botanical name of the genus to which it belongs is *Chamaecyparis*, meaning 'false cypress'. It is distinguished from the true cypresses (*Cupressus*) by the scale-like leaves on the shoots forming ferny sprays of narrow, flattened tape-like twigs; on the true cypresses these twigs are rounded and cord-like. It can be separated from several rather similar trees by the marked smell of parsley from the crushed leaves.

Lawson's cypress has a rather limited range in nature, being a coastal tree found mostly from south-west Oregon to north-west California, with some areas inland. It lives, therefore, in a damp, foggy atmosphere where frost and extreme heat are rare. Yet there are few parts of the British Isles where it will not grow, even tolerating an urban climate, whose deposit, however, does take the shine and freshness off the foliage.

Lawson's cypress[1] owes it botanical epithet *lawsoniana* to the Edinburgh firm of nurserymen, Peter Lawson and Son, who raised only four plants from a consignment of seeds sent by William Murray from the Sacramento River in 1854. This is surprising, as in this country great quantities of fertile seed are produced on quite young trees. In our nurseries these have produced a great variety of sports – narrow and erect, broad and drooping, dwarf, silver-leaved and gold-leaved. At least fifty distinct kinds have been recorded.

These variations, and the ease with which they may be propagated from cuttings and cultivated, make it the conifer *par excellence* for the landscape of municipal parks. In America the timber is valuable, but the tree is as yet not much grown in our forests. The demand for foliage by florists is a considerable commercial asset.

One of the last trees to achieve recognition as a useful timber producer was the ill-fated Jeffrey's introduction, *Pinus contorta*,[2] the lodge-pole pine; it was nearly a century after he sent it from the Siskiyou Mountains in 1853 before its value as a tree that would grow on the poorest sites was generally realised. It is a two-needled pine with a very wide geographical distribution within which it varies so greatly that the two extremes have in the past been regarded by some authorities as distinct species. For our purposes, the form introduced by Jeffreys is used. After its introduction it was grown on a small scale and its value was not appreciated until the 1939–45 war, when seed was not available. In 1946 seed from the proper source was again imported. By 1951 it had become classified by the Fores-

[1] In the U.S.A. the name is usually Port Orford cedar.
[2] It had already been discovered by the American explorers Lewis and Clark in 1805.

try Commission as a major species in their planting programme. Particularly when young, it is the least attractive of the forest pines.

Mention has already been made of large conifers, such as the monkey-puzzle and wellingtonia, which, as park and purely ornamental trees of wide distribution in the countryside, give individuality to the scene. There are one or two others, none of which come from the American continent.

First came the deodar, a true cedar (*Cedrus deodara*). The name, from the Sanskrit, means 'tree of a god'. The tree is of graceful form, with a lax, drooping leader and pendulous tips to the branches, quite unlike the rigidity of other cedars. This enables it to withstand without damage – unlike the Lebanon cedar – the heavy falls of snow that it suffers in its home, the western Himalayas, between 6,000 and 8,000 feet. A number of attempts to introduce it were made between 1820 and 1830, but apparently none succeeded, possibly owing to the heat of the districts through which they were carried causing mildew and rotting. Probably the first to succeed was the Hon. Leslie Melville, who brought home seed in 1831; within a few years, further introductions were made from which 100,000 seedlings were planted by the Crown in some of the royal forests. For some reason, they had all died before the end of the century, which is puzzling as few parks or large gardens are today without thriving specimens, the tallest having reached 120 feet – examples over 100 feet being not unusual. The native timber is valued, but the tree is little grown in our own forests. This cedar, unlike the others we have, is very shy in producing seeds.

The Atlas cedar, the only tree from the Atlas Mountains to thrive in this country, was first brought here in about 1843 by Lord Somers and raised at Eastnor Park, Herefordshire, and probably by his friends elsewhere. It is a vigorous, stiffly-formed tree, with a strong tendency to produce grey and even blue leaved forms, of the utmost beauty. Producing fertile seeds, of great hardiness, and tolerating urban atmosphere better than most conifers, *Cedrus atlantica* has been planted on a considerable scale as an ornamental tree, particularly during the last few decades, and must by now be the commonest cedar in Britain. Specimens have already exceeded a hundred feet. The timber is good, and some experiments have been made with growing the tree in our forests.

Finally, there are some conifers from Japan that emerged during the Victorian era and must be included – with one exception – as minor stars of its galaxy. Japan had for centuries been a country closed to foreigners, until in 1858 they were given greater access. Two years later John Gould Veitch – a younger member of the famous family of nurserymen – visited the country attached to the staff of the British envoy. He sent home many trees, shrubs and plants that have subsequently taken their place in British gardens. Two conifers that he introduced, long known as retinosporas, were planted widely in Victorian and Edwardian gardens; particularly were they used to decorate cemeteries. One was the Hinoki (*Chamaecyparis obtusa*), with leaves like a Lawson's cypress, but rather fatter and blunt-pointed. This is an important timber tree in Japan, growing to 120 feet, but with us it is seldom more than 35 feet high. The Japanese have selected many forms, some of them rather strange. Several of these are found in our gardens. The other is the Sawara cypress (*Chamaecyparis pisifera*).[1] This has more pointed leaves than the Hinoki, and like it has sported into many forms, one of which, 'Squarrosa', with feathery leaves, was imported in 1843. This tree is of no value in forestry and never reaches any great sizes; 35 to 40 feet is normally its limit, but it is common in ornamental plantations.

John Gould's third conifer is the Japanese larch, *Larix leptolepis*, which is an important forest tree. When young it grows with much greater vigour than the European larch. Like some of the Californian conifers it grows wild only in a small area, being restricted to mountains in the centre of Honshu Island. At first, no one bothered with it either for ornament or forestry, but in 1883 still another Duke of Atholl brought home seed from Japan. His trees grew so well that within a few decades Japanese larch was on the way to becoming a major species in our forests. It is very similar to the common larch, except in winter when plantations spectacularly light up the mountains with the orange-red glow of their bare twigs.

Japanese has hybridised with European larch. The result, called Dunkeld larch (*Larix eurolepis*), is also being planted.

It is an astonishing thought that the pioneering collections of principally three men, Douglas, Lobb and Veitch, all of whose work was completed between 1824 and 1861, should within the subsequent century have transformed the whole nature of the woodland and park landscape of the British Isles, as well as wide areas in other parts of the world (Plate 47).

THE VICTORIAN LANDSCAPE

The protean Sir Joseph Paxton (1801–65), particularly since William Robinson wrote of his design for the Crystal Palace that 'at Sydenham we have the greatest modern example of the waste of enormous means in making hideous a fine piece of ground', has been regarded as a clever

[1] *Pisifera*, pea-bearing, from the tiny cones.

botanical gardener, an ingenious inventor of glass-houses, and a plutocrat of the railway age. In fact, as a pioneer in the design of what have now become local authority parks, he had considerable and good influence on landscape design, utilising trees to fine advantage – his influence extended beyond his work through men such as Edward Milner, who worked under him and later, on his own, from between 1850 and 1884 'completed many of the finest (landscape) works that have ever been produced'. Some of these were Bodnant, Hartsholme Hall and Heighinton Hall (the latter two in Lincolnshire). His son, H. E. Milner, F.L.S., A.M.I.M.E., continued in the same style and published *The Art and Practice of Landscape Gardening* illustrated with deplorable etchings. Others of the Paxtonian era included Robert Marnock (1800–89), who wrote for Loudon's *Gardener's Magazine*, and looked back to Repton and whose landscape work ranged from re-designing the gardens at Bretby Hall in the 1830s to planning William Robinson's Gravetye garden in 1884. A protégé of Paxton's was Edward Kemp.

Paxton, however, was in a class above these men, and he had a singular knowledge of trees. He was foreman of the arboretum at the Horticultural Society's garden at Chiswick when, in 1826, the Duke of Devonshire invited him to become gardener at Chatsworth. In 1829 he had formed, in the already richly wooded park, a collection of conifers (introductions, particularly from western North America, were now coming in fast). In 1834 'a very complete arboretum' was begun. A number of the early trees still remain.

Paxton's landscaping work, outside Chatsworth, began at least as early as 1842, when he was concerned with others in producing the plan for Prince's Park, Liverpool. He was then described as 'Garden Architect and Landscape Gardener, Chatsworth'. Later in that decade he designed a long strip of well-wooded land on the Menai Strait.

Probably his most important and influential work was Birkenhead Park, begun in 1844. This, as was general in his best works, was in the tradition of Repton, modified to some extent by Loudon's 'gardenesque'. Its future influence comes from the remarkable circulatory traffic system. This was seen by the American landscaper, F. L. Olmstead, in 1852, and again in 1858 when he was working on the design for the Central Park in New York, which has 'the most articulated system of circulation of any park before or since', inspired by Paxton.

If Paxton's most permanent and beneficial influence on the landscape was the style he set for the planting in public parks, it must be remembered that he was concerned with the revival of the formal, or perhaps more appropriately called geometrical Italianate style of garden associated with Sir Charles Barry (1795–1860) and W. A. Nesfield (1793–1881) that was to rule in the mid-nineteenth century. A study of that period, *Garden Architecture and Landscape Gardening* by John Arthur Hughes (1866), shows no understanding whatsoever of the use of trees. W. A. Nesfield was, it is true, concerned with the design of the Arboretum in the Royal Botanic Gardens, Kew, but his most interesting contributions to the landscape were his avenues using unusual trees. Such is his long, and dramatically effective avenue of sombre ilexes at Kew linking the huge, glassy mass of the palm house with the placid view over the Thames, at the centre of which stands Syon House in isolated distinction. At Broxwood Court, where he was responsible for the gardens, a wide avenue of conifers streams with great originality across the Herefordshire countryside.

The Victorian period, indeed, saw a revival of avenue planting. Repton eventually expressed the opinion that avenues, providing that they curved, were permissible. Certainly the double avenue of limes following the meandering drive for three miles in Clumber Park, planted in 1840, follows this principle – and holds the record for the longest English avenue (Plate 48).

The genesis of the woodland and wild garden also belongs to the Victorian age, though it did not really gain momentum until the introductions from western China that came with the opening of the twentieth century. G. F. Wilson began his famous Wisley garden as early as 1878. The later years of the century saw the developments of the Cornish landscape gardens, full of trees, of which Glendurgan is an example (Plate 49). In England there were parts of Dropmore and Westonbirt which were much more than collections of trees (Plate 50). In Ireland there were numerous examples, such as Castlewellan, which combined a mixture of Victorian formality with free planting of conifers (Plate 51). Miss Jekyll began her appropriately named Munstead Wood in 1896.

CHAPTER NINE

The Twentieth Century

THE EARLY DECADES of this century brought about a greater change in the woodland scene than had ever occurred before. The whole concept of forestry was fundamentally altered, and after centuries of decrease the area of land growing trees at last began to increase. The planting of ornamental trees underwent a similar revolution.

It seems best to take the events that brought about these changes in chronological order, which means that ornamental planting must first be considered.

Due principally to the activities of French Jesuit missionaries working in western China and Tibet, who were ardent naturalists, the extraordinarily rich flora of this region was becoming known in Europe, though few of the plants that they discovered were introduced to Europe other than as herbarium specimens. The principal workers in this field were the Frenchmen, J. P. A. David (1826–1900), J. M. Delavay (1834–95), P. G. Farges (1844–1912) and J. A. Soulié (1858–1905). Their specimens went to Paris. There were, too, Russians working from what was then St Petersburg. An Irishman, Augustine Henry (1857–1930), posted to the Chinese Maritime Customs at Ichang by the great gorges of the Yangtze River, though not a botanist, in 1886 sent off a box of plants to the Royal Botanic Gardens at Kew with a request that they would name them for him – an ignorant amateur who was amazed at the rich flora around him. The authorities at Kew encouraged him to pursue his studies and to send more. Henry in due course became an authority on one of the richest floras of the temperate world.

Though British plant collectors, such as Douglas, Fortune, the Lobbs and J. H. Veitch, had searched much of the temperate world, none had been – largely on account of political reasons – into western China. The nurseryman Veitch had sent out Charles Maries (*c.* 1851–1902) in 1879, but he had stopped short at the entry to the Ichang gorges in the belief that there was little worth collecting beyond them.

At about this time a new style of gardening was being evolved – in some ways a development of Uvedale Price's ideas. The woodland garden of ornamental trees mixed with our natives was being underplanted with flowering shrubs, herbaceous plants and particularly bulbs which were of a fairly permanent nature. The trees and shrubs in particular grew and improved year by year with little attention. An outstanding pioneer of this type of gardening – which was in some ways a development of the very informal Cornish and western Scottish gardens, was G. F. Wilson (1822–1902), who bought an estate of neglected woods in Surrey and under its cover achieved great success with plants often considered difficult. The result is now incorporated in the Royal Horticultural Society's garden at Wisley.

There were, of course, many trees and shrubs already available for this type of garden, which greatly interested certain of what might be called the new plutocracy.

The last of the great firm of Veitch, Sir Harry (1840–1924), realised the vast possibilities of the Chinese flora now in the course of discovery, and of which he saw specimens sent to Kew by Henry. In 1899 he despatched Ernest Henry Wilson (1876–1930) to rendezvous with Henry, by now at Szemao in south-west Yunnan. A principal objective was to collect seeds of the davidia or handkerchief tree (*Davidia involucrata*), now well known in our gardens. Wilson pressed on past the point where Maries faltered and was thus the first professional plant collector to break through into a huge area whose temperate flora was of the utmost richness.

In the United States a comparable enthusiast was Charles Sprague Sargent (1842–1907) of the Arnold Arboretum of Harvard University (who himself travelled and collected in Japan) for whom Wilson subsequently collected.

At first the proceeds were distributed by Veitch. Later expeditions were financed by private syndicates and it is to them that we owe the valuable additions to our gardens and woodlands brought home by Wilson's successors of whom the most notable were George Forrest (1873–1932) and Frank Kingdon-Ward (1885–1958). From America came J. F. Rock (1884–1962).

Until the Second World War cut off communications with so much of this area, the range of woodland plants was increased enormously. During

61. The new landscape, Scotland: near the Gorge of Corriehalloch, Ross-shire.

62. The new landscape, Wales: Gwydr Forest, Caernarvonshire.

63. The new landscape, Northern Ireland: Tollymore.

the same period, interesting introductions were also made from South America and New Zealand.

The great era of the creation and augmentation of these woodland gardens, in which the British, with their long tradition of the effective planting of trees, excelled, was, therefore, during the closing years of the nineteenth and the opening decades of the twentieth centuries.

During that time – to name at random only a few estates – the great collections, most beautifully laid out for beauty at all seasons, at Weston-birt (Plate 52), Bodnant (Plate 53), Caerhays, Sheffield Park, Borde Hill, Hergest Croft (Plate 54), Nymans, Wakehurst, Crarae, Benmore (Plate 55), Rowallane (Plate 56), and one of the most recent, the Savill Gardens in Windsor Park, were either created or developed beyond recognition from the older, more formal arboreta and pineta. Ireland, too, is particularly rich in woodland gardens. The number of smaller examples is legion; for instance, the famous, largely formal, garden at Hidcote includes a small, most delightful and interesting woodland area. What we may call this new British (for now the Scots and Irish were involved) style of woodland and even forest garden spread far and wide; there are examples, using largely the same range of trees that grow naturally in temperate climates both in the New World and the southern hemisphere, where, for example, W. Douglas Cook at Eastwoodhill in New Zealand's North Island has made a woodland garden and collection of trees on the grandest of scales (Plate 57).

This period, at a time when forestry and the commercial production of timber was at as low an ebb as it had ever been, was one in which there was, on the contrary, a great deal of interest in trees, and during which experience was gained, by enthusiastic arboriculturists rather than fores-ters, of the trees that were within a short while to be of great economic importance. Evidence of this was the publication between 1906 and 1913 of the seven volumes of *The Trees of Great Britain and Ireland* by H. J. Elwes (1846–1922) and Augustine Henry, then home from China. This massive work, on the grand scale of a Loudon, has not yet been superseded, though now needing at least considerable revision. Another landmark was W. J. Bean's *Trees and Shrubs Hardy in the British Isles*, whose two volumes, subsequently increased and revised, were published in 1914. Such forestry education as there was was largely directed to training for the forests of our then Empire, and produced technical men of the first quality.

The beginning of the century, as a part of this growing enthusiasm for trees, saw the first serious efforts to clothe the desolate spoil heaps of our industrial districts with trees. For instance, the Midland Re-Afforestation Association was formed early in the century. Its activities were described by Marcus Woodward in 1905. A survey was made of the Black Country pit banks by P. E. Martineau. Here and there success was achieved. A good example was – and still is – Wednesbury Park, which in the 1890s was a desolate spot, but by 1905 was developing into the interesting place it was later to become.

Owing to public lack of enthusiasm and damage, failure was frequent. However, it was a pioneer effort. Subsequent reclamations, such as those to conceal ironstone workings in Northamptonshire and old pit banks in the Forest of Dean, have been on an extensive scale and have transformed desert-like wastes, which would, if neglected, have by degrees turned into scrub.

But to our own once great woodlands, often full of magnificent, but over-aged trees, producing such little timber as was used on a small scale by old methods for old crafts, little attention was paid. The enthusiasm of rich industrialists for sport prevented the felling of many ancient woods, which were allowed to decay. The financial difficulties of traditional land-lords caused them to fell and sell at a low price, without replanting. A handful of enthusiasts saw the danger of neglecting our forests (C. P. Ackers recalls that, in his youth, some of the Deputy Surveyors of the Royal Forests were still being appointed on the grounds of family con-nections or valued political services) and campaigned for an active forest policy. Some, fighting against almost universal prejudice, began planting the Californian conifers as forest trees in their woodlands.

The largest individual owner of forest and woodland remained the Crown, operating through the Office of Woods, Forests and Land Revenue of the Crown. This followed an exceedingly cautious, if slightly progres-sive, policy. From 1893 to 1912 the Commissioner, Sir Stafford Howard, in spite of difficulties owing to the complex laws of the New and Dean Forests, did make some progress. Sir William Schlich, a scientific forester with much experience in India, was called in to prepare plans of manage-ment. Further woodlands were acquired, such as the Inverliver estate in Argyll, Tintern in Monmouthshire and Hafod Fawr in North Wales. A training school for foresters was established at Parkend in the Forest of Dean in 1904.

So far as British forestry in general was concerned, the Board of Agriculture set up a Select Committee on Forestry, which sat from 1885 to 1887. It was followed by a whole series of other official committees, commissions and boards which looked at every aspect of forestry, such as the training of foresters, the provision of forest holdings for those in over-congested industrial areas, and the planting of forests, to combat land erosion.[1]

In 1912 the Board divided England and Wales into five districts, based on scientific institutions. These were Armstrong College at Newcastle-on-Tyne, University College of North Wales, Oxford University, Cambridge University and the Royal Agricultural College at Cirencester. A comparable Board of Agriculture for Scotland made little real progress with forestry, though teaching was carried on in the universities at Aberdeen and Edinburgh. Rather more was done in Ireland, when three State forests were formed.

In 1910 some assistance had been given to private forestry in the Finance Act, which made concessions to woodland owners in respect of death duties. And during this period, Manchester Corporation, with its own funds, pioneered the afforestation of the catchment area around Thirlmere in the Lake District. This great achievement, bitterly opposed by preservationists as destroying the bleak beauties of the district, is now regarded as one of the loveliest scenes in Lakeland.

In sum total, however, wonderfully little was effected, though a general opinion was evolved that some system of State forestry should be brought into existence to supplement the considerable area of woodlands still in private hands, and to afforest (in the modern sense of the word) the wide areas of the British Isles which would support trees, but which were otherwise derelict, and so reduce, if only slightly, our huge import bill for timber.

The situation was summed up by E. P. Stebbing, of Edinburgh University:

'At various periods in the last score of years Royal Commissions have examined the question (and numerous witnesses), and have issued the results of their labours in voluminous Blue-Books. . . . But they have remained a dead letter so far as any practical application of the suggestions they have contained with reference to afforestation on a large scale in the interests of the nation.'

Those words were published in 1916. By then, the country was at war – a war, it will be remembered, that was in its opening stages considered quite light-heartedly – and once again enemy blockade was to cut us off from our supplies of timber. No longer was it oak for our ships that was

[1] On occasion, financial aid was obtained from the Development Commission.

lost, but, for example, softwoods for our pit props, of which huge quantities had been imported.

A timber famine followed. Those who had for years pointed out that this might well happen were tragically justified. The timber that we had, good and even bad, was felled on a scale hitherto unknown, with such urgency that there was no time to replant. Never had our woods been in such a state of devastation; the traces of our old forest and woodland landscape that remained in 1914 were largely obliterated by 1918. Even in our park-land, most of the great oaks that were sound fell to the axe.

This shock brought action. Though, for immediate purposes, it was sixty or seventy years too late, the lucubrations of the committees, the scientific experience of the few scholastic institutions interested in forestry, and the ardent activities of our two societies, had contributed material of considerable use in evolving a national policy. Further, within the Forestry Division of the Board of Agriculture for England and Wales, as well as in the comparable bodies for Ireland and Scotland, a nucleus of young men had grown up dedicated to the service of forestry.

Thus, when in 1916 a Forestry Sub-Committee was set up within the Ministry of Reconstruction under Sir Francis Acland, spurred on now by an even greater sense of urgency than in our previous times of shortage, there was sufficient, if still inadequate, experience of both theory and practice to evolve a workable Report, issued in 1918. This embodied three fundamental proposals.

First, that a body should be created with funds to survey, purchase, lease and plant land, and to administer these areas.

Second, that the care of forestry throughout the British Isles should be centred in this Authority instead of being, as it then was, divided among several departments.

Third, that the Authority should be able to make grants to private individuals or public bodies for replanting or newly afforesting land, such undertakings to be carried out in accordance with approved plans and conditions.

In 1919 the proposed authority, known as the Forestry Commission, was set up. To it were transferred all the Crown Forests with the exception of Windsor. In December of that year the body made its first planting, which was of beech and European larch, at Eggesford Forest in Devon.

In Northern Ireland, 1920 saw the transference of responsibility for forestry to the Ministry of Agriculture. In what is now the Irish Republic, the government took charge in 1922.

From the first the new body and its policy met with difficulties unknown in earlier periods of planting. There was considerable public opposition to its extensive use of conifers, but quick-growing softwoods were economically what was needed, and would grow where our traditional hardwoods would not. It was suggested that mammal, bird and plant would suffer. That has proved not to be so; in fact owing to the wise and all-embracing policy of the Commission, particularly as it has developed in recent years, the reverse is the case. A sense of urgency and enthusiasm unusual in any government-controlled body inevitably led to many mistakes and plantings that were both unsightly and unsatisfactory, both by the Commission and the landowners it assisted.

Apart from those who regarded the new forestry as – for want of a better phrase – in bad taste, two comparatively new hazards were present. By 1912, it was estimated, the rabbit, most destructive of all mammals to young trees, had, except for certain other rodents, probably become the most vigorous, prolific and abundant animal in the British Isles. And the North American grey squirrel, introduced here in the late years of the nineteenth century, and another enemy of trees, was showing signs of an alarming increase.

The problems and growing pains of the new forestry, both State and private, were daunting. Slowly they were being overcome, when, with the outbreak of war in 1939, it received an almost overwhelming blow. With improved methods of extraction, the more remote woods that had escaped the 1914–18 fellings were slaughtered. Much more timber was felled before it was mature.

After the peace of 1945 planting continued on an increased scale. In the subsequent period during which the once much vaunted legislation of town and country planning has become little more than restrictive, our new forests and woodlands have been the solitary positive contribution to the beauty and interest of the landscape, quite apart from the sociological and public amenity aspects – the former being of important consequence in, for example, the depressed areas of Wales and the border counties (Plate 58) and Scotland, while the latter, with the provision of forest parks and the opening of public access to many acres of woodlands, has given a new and healthy facet to the numerous pleasures of the automobile-borne urban population.

Economically, the increasing production of the woods is being absorbed in factories producing pulp for paper, for the making of materials such as chip-board and for saw timber.

It may seem tedious to have recounted, even in outline, these political, financial and economic factors governing the revival of our forests. It cannot be over-emphasised, however, that since the day when the monastic woodlands were sold in the sixteenth century, these are the factors that have controlled the very existence of our woodland scenery. Compared with forestry carried out under pressure from these factors, that of amenity planting, largely restricted to the eighteenth and early nineteenth centuries, is small.

It is, however, with the resultant landscape that we are mostly concerned. Now the new forests are maturing, we are learning that they are not the green monotony that was foretold. British geology, the countour of the land, the qualities of the soil and the rainfall vary so hugely within comparatively small areas that good forestry results in a comparable variety in selection of species and treatment. The pattern and colour of the forests around Lake Vyrnwy on a winter's day is one which, under the ever-changing Welsh skies, is of infinite variety (Plate 59). There is the smouldering red of the bare Japanese larch, the bright green of the Norway spruce, the more sombre colour of the Sitka spruce, the grey of the noble fir, all mingled with patches of our native trees and green areas for grazing sheep. And, as a contrasting example, is the calm formality of the pines on the once bleak and arid Thetford Chase.

But the new scenes are there for all to see, changing over the years, from planting to harvest – to use a fashionable term, the end-product of the long history that I have attempted to describe (Plates 60–63).

And it must be remembered that our country landscape, more made by man than that of most other nations, is consequent upon economic pressures; the aesthetic pleasures that it gives are due to the quest for pounds, shillings and pence and not, except for a small portion of our area, the production of aesthetes or the preservation of antiquarians – admirable though these activities are.

Today there seems little doubt that a world timber shortage is round the corner and, as timber users and importers on a huge scale, we must look to the future – which is totally different from the past when we failed so disastrously to anticipate first the need of oak for our ships and later other timbers for our saw mills and coal mines.

Most timber today is required for processing – though there is a continued demand for good quality saw-timber. Even so, good oak butts go today for veneer rather than structural work. There is an increasing demand for timber to be mashed into pulp for paper, or to be broken down and reconstituted into standardised forms of sheet.

Ranking above the need for wood is that for food. Our finest hardwoods require, if they are to grow at their best and produce fine quality wood, the very land that is essential for food. Further, in our small islands land today is so valuable that it must never be idle – even the poorer quality of the type that we can now use for forestry.

Conifers alone, particularly those from western North America, will both make good timber on the poorer soil where hardwoods will not thrive, and will produce saleable timber at a far greater speed, giving a much speedier financial return on the heavy capital outlay made on the land.

On what today would be considered good forestry land, oak takes as much as a century and a half to produce fine quality timber. In that period, a good conifer will produce two mature crops, each of much greater volume, whose final total value at present-day prices is about four times that of the oak.

'Elementary, my dear Watson', as Sherlock Holmes is reputed to have said (but in fact never did), are the conclusions to be reached from these facts. Our woodlands in the future must be within a matrix of planted conifers instead, as they were for so long, in one of oak.

Within that matrix will be many areas of other trees where conditions permit: for example, ash for sports goods, such as tennis rackets, sweet chestnut for pales – possibly in the future birch for the uses that it already fulfils in Scandinavia. And areas for nature reserves, camping grounds and those other purposes classified as amenity. And outside the woodlands – particularly in our towns – parks and street trees must be used and planted and maintained with all the knowledge and understanding (and it is surprisingly little) and the use of new material that we have acquired in the present century.

In our restless world, Lord Beaconsfield's observation is relevant: 'You may tire of mountains and rivers, you may tire of the sea, but you can never tire of trees.' That we may continue to have a healthy abundance of such unending joys, their planting, cultivation and harvesting must unendingly be deeply and logically considered.

Glossary

IT IS UNFORTUNATELY IMPOSSIBLE to avoid the use of some words which have a specialised meaning, justified by long usage, when connected with trees and forestry, as well as other words of more technical type. These are rather loosely defined below.

ARBORETUM: a collection of living trees of all kinds; the plural is arboreta.

ARBORICULTURE: the cultivation of trees of all kinds for amenity purposes as distinct from silviculture (q.v.).

BOLE: that part of the trunk of a tree below the first main branch.

BROAD-LEAVED (of a class of trees): a not always literal description of any dicotyledonous tree (also called a hardwood) as distinct from conifers.

BURR: a large, woody swelling on the trunk or main branches of a tree; the elaborate graining of such a growth (as in walnut) sometimes adds considerable value to the timber.

CLONE: the sum total of plants propagated vegetatively (i.e. by cuttings, budding or grafting) from one individual (e.g. 'Cox's Orange Pippin' apple).

CONIFER: in general terms trees whose fruit is a cone in which the seeds (usually winged) are loosely held between scales. The structure of the wood is distinct from that of hardwoods and includes canals containing resin, absent from hardwoods.

COPPICE: a tree which is at regular intervals cut down to ground level which causes the growth of several stout poles, used, for example, in fencing. The operation is called coppicing. Most conifers will not produce such growths.

COPSE: strictly, a wood that is coppiced, but in practice a small wood.

DECIDUOUS: of a tree, dropping all the leaves annually.

DOTARD: a tree that has lost its branches so that only the trunk and a few twigs remain.

EVERGREEN: a tree bearing leaves that last more than one year, so that it is always leafy. The leaves of such trees, however, do not usually persist for more than a few years.

EXOTIC: introduced from overseas, i.e. not present in our natural vegetation at the time when our link with the Continent was cut by the sea.

FIR: now usually applied to the genera *Abies*, the silver firs; *Picea*, the spruce firs;

and *Pseudotsuga*, the Douglas firs, but in the English vernacular long applied to Scots pine *Pinus*.

FOREST: formerly a royal hunting ground (not necessarily thickly wooded) coming under the savage forest laws; now generally applied (particularly by the Forestry Commission) to any large area of trees.

GENUS: the lowest category of plant classification (plural, genera), e.g. *Pinus*, *Acer*, and composed of species.

HARDWOOD: see broad-leaved, and like that term, not always justified in practice.

HEART-WOOD: the hard, matured and dead wood around the centre of the trunk, making the most valuable timber.

HYBRID: in general a cross between two species of the same genus which often has some qualities – good and bad – of both parents. Some hybrids are outstandingly better for human purposes than species; for example, certain hybrid poplars grow quicker and produce more timber than any true species. Hybrids rarely come true from seed and must be propagated vegetatively – that is, by rooting cuttings or grafting.

INTRODUCED (of a tree): not native, i.e. an exotic species brought from overseas and cultivated in our islands.

MAIDEN: a tree allowed to grow on a single stem or trunk and neither pollarded nor copsed.

NATIVE: a species of tree growing in our islands before they were detached from the Continent, the opposite to exotic.

NATURALISED: an exotic species of tree that has seeded itself and produces continuing generations in this country without the aid of man.

PINETUM (plural pineta): now generally taken to be a collection of growing trees restricted to conifers.

POLLARD: a tree regularly cut back at a height out of the reach of grazing stock to produce poles, e.g. riverside willows.

REGENERATION, NATURAL: a forester's term for trees that have arisen from and around their parents without having been sown by man; natural reproduction would be a better description.

SAPWOOD: the outer wood of a tree trunk or branch, still to some extent alive, as distinct from the dead heart-wood, and less valuable as timber.

SILVICULTURE: the cultivation of trees in woods for the production of timber, as distinct from arboriculture (q.v.).

SOFTWOOD: a general term applied to conifers, as distinct from hardwood (q.v.), whose timber is usually, but by no means always, comparatively soft.

SPECIES: the fundamental unit in the botanical classification of plants, frequently, but not always, described by a Latin epithet. For example, the botanical name for the beech is *Fagus sylvatica*. *Fagus* is the generic name, finally determined by the epithet *sylvatica* (loving woods) to indicate the species.

VARIETY: a minor form within a species which arises in nature, but does not deviate from the type sufficiently to justify specific rank.

Bibliography

The dates given are those of the editions consulted. Poetry quoted is from standard editions.

Ackers, C. P., *Practical British Forestry*, 1948.
  'Looking back', *Quarterly Journal of Forestry*, LI, 1957.
Addison, Rt Hon. J., *Remarks on Several Parts of Italy, 1701–3*, 1705.
Aelfric, Glossary, *Grammatica Latino-Saxonica*, 1659.
Albion, R. G., *Forests and Sea Power*, 1926.
Allen, B. S., *Tides in English Taste*, 1937.
Amherst, the Hon. A., *A History of Gardening in England*, 1895.
Anderson, M. L., *Natural Woodlands of Great Britain*, 1932.
  The Selection of Tree Species, 1950.
  'Distribution of the sessile oak in the New Forest', *Forestry*, XXIV, 1951.
  'Early hardwood planting in Ireland', *Scottish Forestry*, 6, 1952.
  'Wistman's Wood', *Transactions of Botanical Society of Edinburgh*, XXXV, 1952–53.
Anon., Review of *The Planter's Guide*, *Blackwood's Magazine*, 1828.
Ashbee, P., *The Bronze Age Barrow in Britain*, 1960.
Ashton, T. S., *The Industrial Revolution*, 1948.
Aubrey, J., *Natural History of Wiltshire*, 1845 ed.
Balfour, F. R. S., 'The original Scottish horse chestnuts', *Scottish Forestry Journal*, 47, 1933.
Bazeley, M. L., 'Extent of the English forest in the thirteenth century', *Transactions Royal Historical Society*, 1921.
Bean, W. J., *Trees and Shrubs Hardy in the British Isles*, 1929–36.
Beresford, M., *History on the Ground*, 1957.
Birch, T., *History of the Royal Society*, 1756.
Blaikie, T. (ed. Birrell, F.), *Diary of a Scotch Gardener*, 1931.
Blair, P. H., *Roman Britain and Early England 55 B.C. to A.D. 871*, 1963.
Blunt, W., *The Art of Botanical Illustration*, 1950.
Boon, G. C., *Roman Silchester*, 1957.
Box, B. A., *The English Parsonage*, 1964.
Bridger, J., *Report to Navy Board*, 1696.
Burke, Rt Hon. E., *A philosophical enquiry into the origin of our ideas of the sublime and beautiful*, 1757.

Byng, J., Viscount Torrington, *The Torrington Diaries* (ed. C. B. Andrewes), 1934–8.

Cadman, W. A., 'The New Forest', *Forestry*, XXXV, 1962.

Cantor, L. M., 'The Medieval Parks of South Staffordshire', *Birmingham Archaeological Society Transactions*, 80, 1965.

Cardigan, The Earl of, *The Wardens of Savernake Forest*, 1949.

Carritt, F., *Calendar of British Taste*, 1600–1800.

Chadwick, G. F., *The Works of Sir Joseph Paxton*, 1961.

Chambers, W., *A Dissertation on Oriental Gardening*, 1772.

Charnock, J., *An History of Marine Architecture*, 1801.

Chase, I. W. U., *Horace Walpole, gardenist*, 1943.

Clapham, A. R., Tutin, T. G., and Warburg, E. F., *Flora of the British Isles*, 1952.

Clark, H. F., *The English Landscape Garden*, 1948.

(and others), *England and the Mediterranean Tradition*, 1945.

Cobbett, W., *The American Gardener*, 1821.

Collingwood, G. H., and Brush, W. D., *Knowing your Trees*, 1949.

Cook, M., *The Manner of Raising, Ordering and Improving Forest Trees*, 1724.

Corner, H. H., 'A History of Land Use in the Borders', *Scottish Forestry*, 17, 1963.

Cornish, V., *Historic Thorn Trees in the British Isles*, 1941.

The Churchyard Yew and Immortality, 1946.

Cox, E. H. M., *History of Gardening in Scotland*, 1935.

Plant Hunting in China, 1945.

Cox, J. C., *The Royal Forests of England*, 1905.

Creed, Sir T., and others, *Report of the Forest of Dean Committee*, 1958.

Crossley, F. H., *Timber Building in England*, 1951.

Dallaway, Rev. J., *Supplementary Anecdotes*, 1798.

Dallimore, W., *Holly, Yew and Box*, 1908.

and Jackson, B., *A Handbook of Coniferae*, 1948.

Dandy, J. E., *List of British Vascular Plants*, 1958.

Darby, H. C., *The Domesday Geography of Eastern England*, 1952.

(editor), *A Historical Geography of England Before A.D. 1800*, 1930.

and Terret, H. B., *The Domesday Geography of Midland England*, 1954.

Davison, J. E., and Gardner, R. C. B., 'The History of the Royal Forestry Society of England and Wales', *Quarterly Journal of Forestry*, LI, 1957.

Dean, W., *Croome d'Abitot, to which are attached Hortus Croomensis and observations on the propagation of exotics*, 1824.

Defoe, D. (ed. Cole, G. D. H.), *A tour thro' the whole island of Britain*, 1927.

Dent, J., *The Quest for Nonsuch*, 1962.

Dimbleby, G. W., *The Development of British Heathlands and their Soil*, 1962.

Downing, A. J., (ed. Waugh, F. A.), *A Treatise on the Theory and Practice of Landscape Gardening Adapted to North America*, 1921.

Dunham, K., *The Gun Trade of Birmingham*, 1955.

Edlin, H. L., *Woodland Crafts in Britain*, 1949.

'Early State encouragement of forestry', *Quarterly Journal of Forestry*, LXI, 1957.

England's Forests, 1958.

Ekwall, E., *The Concise Oxford Dictionary of Place Names*, 1960.

Eley, C., *Gardening for the Twentieth Century*, 1923.

Elwes, H. J., and Henry, A., *Trees of Great Britain and Ireland*, 1906–12.

Evelyn, J., *Sylva*, 1729.

(ed. Hunter, J.), *Sylva*, 1786.

(ed. de Beer, E. S.), *Diary*, 1955.

Fay, C. R., *Huskisson and his Age*, 1951.

Fleming, J., *Robert Adam and his Circle*, 1962.

Fletcher, J. S., *Cistercians in Yorkshire*, 1919.

Forestry Commission, *Census of Woodlands, 1947–49*, 1952.

Exotic Forest Trees in Britain, 1952.

Fox, Sir C., *The Personality of Britain*, 1959.

Gilpin, W., *Remarks on Forest Scenery*, 1791.

Gilpin, W. S., *Practical Hints for Landscape Gardening*, 1835.

Godwin, H., 'Pollen Analyses and the Forest History of England', *New Phytologist*, XXXIX, 1940.

History of the British Flora, 1956.

Gothein, M. L. (trans. Archer-Hind), *A History of Garden Art*, 1922.

Gras, N. S. B., *The Early English Customs System*, 1928.

Graves, Rev. R., *Recollections of some Particulars in the Life of William Shenstone, Esq.*, 1788.

Green, D., *Blenheim Palace*, 1951.

Gardener to Queen Anne, 1956.

Grundy, G. B., *Saxon Charters of Worcestershire*, 1931.

'Ancient woodlands of Gloucester', *Transactions Bristol and Gloucester Archaeological Society*, 58, 1936.

Haddington, Earl of, *A Short Treatise on Forest Trees*, 1756.

Hadfield, M., *British Trees*, 1957.

Gardening in Britain, 1960.

'The cedar, its name and introduction to Britain', *Quarterly Journal of Forestry*, LVIII, 1964.

and J., *Gardens of Delight*, 1964.

Hart, C. E., *Royal Forest: A History of Deans Woods as Producer of Timber*, 1966.

Harvey, A. G., *Douglas of the Firs*, 1947.

Harvey, J., *Gothic England, 1300–1500*, 1948.

The Plantagenets, 1959.

Highet, G., *Poets in a Landscape*, 1957.

Hill, J., *The Curious Gardener*, 1932.

Hilton, R. H., *The Economic Development of some Leicestershire Estates in the 14th and 15th century*, 1947.

Hogarth, W. (ed. Burke, J.), *The Analysis of Beauty*, 1955.

Home, Henry, Lord Kames, *Elements of Criticism*, 1762.

Honey, W. B., *English Glass*, 1946.

Honour, H., *Chinoiserie: the Vision of Cathay*, 1961.

Hudson, D., and Luckhurst, K. W., *The Royal Society of Arts*, 1954.

Hughes, E., *North Country Life in the Eighteenth Century*, 1952.

Hughes, J. A., *Garden Architecture and Landscape Gardening*, 1866.

Humphreys, A. R., *William Shenstone*, 1937.

Hussey, C., *The Picturesque*, 1927.

Hutchinson, W., *An Excursion to the Lakes*, 1774.

Hyde, H. A., *Welsh Timber Trees*, 1961.

Iljin, M., 'Russian parks of the eighteenth century', *Architectural Review*, 1964.

Izon, J., 'How 16th-century Birmingham got its iron', *Birmingham Post*, 1952.
    'Midland iron works', *Birmingham Post*, 1952.

James, N. D. G., *The Forester's Companion*, 1966.

Jefferson, T. (annotated Betts, E. M.), *Garden Book*, 1944.

Jekyll, G., *Home and Garden*, 1900.

Jessen, K., 'Studies in . . . floral history of Ireland', *Transactions Royal Irish Academy* 52B, 1948–50.

Johnson, G. W., *A History of English Gardening*, 1829.

Johnson, J. T., 'John Jeffrey and the Oregon Association', *Notes From the Royal Botanic Garden, Edinburgh*, XX, 1939.

Jones, E. W., 'Biological flora of the British Isles', *Acer*, L, 1945.
    'Biological flora of the British Isles', *Quercus*, L, 1959.

Kent, A. H., *Veitch's Manual of the Coniferae*, 1900.

Ketton-Cremer, R. W., *Norfolk Portraits*, 1944.

Keynes, G., *John Evelyn*, 1937.

Knight, R. P., *The Landscape*, 1794.
    An Analytical Enquiry into the Principles of Taste, 1808.

Knowles, D., *The Religious Orders in England*, 1948–59.
    The Religious Houses of England, 1940.

Kosminsky, E. A., *Studies in the Agrarian history of England in the Thirteenth Century*, 1956.

Kristeller, P. O., *Eight Philosophers of the Italian Renaissance*, 1965.

Lear, E., *Journal of a Landscape Painter in Corsica*, 1870.

Lennard, R. L., 'Destruction of woodland in eastern counties', *Economic History Review*, XV, 1945.
    Rural England 1086–1135, 1959.

Ligne, Prince de (ed. Ganay, Cte. E. de), *Coup d'oeil sur Beloeil et sur une grande partie des jardins de l'Europe*, 1922.

Loudon, J. C., *Encyclopaedia of Gardening*, 1827.
    Arboretum et Fruticetum Britannicum, 1838.
    (ed.), *The Gardener's Magazine*, 1826–43.
    (ed. Loudon, Mrs), *Encyclopaedia of Gardening*, 1878.

Lousley, J. E. (ed.), *The Changing Flora of Britain*, 1953.

Lowe, J., *The Yew Trees of Great Britain and Ireland*, 1897.

Lyons, Sir H., *The Royal Society*, 1944.

McCracken, E., 'Irish woodlands 1600–1800', *Quarterly Journal of Forestry*, LVII, 1963.

McVean, D. N., 'Biological Flora of the British Isles', *Alnus, Journal of Ecology*, Vol. 41, n.d.

'Regional variation of *Alnus glutinosa* in Britain', *Watsonia*, Vol. IIII, 1953.

Mackay, J., *A Journey through England*, 1722.

Mainwaring, E. W., *Italian Landscape in Eighteenth Century England*, 1925.

Malins, E., *English Landscaping and Literature*, 1966.

Martyn, T., *Flora Rustica*, 1792–94.

Mason, G., *An Essay on Design in Gardening*, 1768.

Mason, Rev. W., *The English Garden*, 1778.

Matthews, J. R., *Origin and Distribution of the British Flora*, 1955.

Mitchell, A. F., 'The biggest trees of many species in Britain', *Journal of the Royal Horticultural Society*, LXXXVIII, 1963.

'The history of the introduction of the European larch to Britain', *Scottish Scottish Forestry*, 17, 1963.

The Dropmore Pinetum, 1963.

Moir, E., *The Discovery of Britain: the English tourists, 1540–1840*, 1964.

Moldenke, H. N. and A. L., *Plants of the Bible*, 1952.

Monk, S. H., *The Sublime*, 1935.

Montagu, Mrs E. (ed. Climenson, E. J.), *Correspondence*, 1906.

Nichols, T., *Observations on Oak Trees*, 1791.

Nicholson, E. M., *Britain's Nature Reserves*, 1957.

Nolhac, P. de (trans. Robinson, F. M.), *The Trianon of Marie Antoinette*, 1925.

North, F. J., *The Evolution of the Bristol Channel*, 1955.

Ogden, H. V. S. and M. S., *English Taste in Landscape in the Eighteenth Century*, 1955.

Ogg, S., *England in the Reigns of James II and William III*, 1955.

Parkinson, J., *Paradisus in sole paradisus terrestris*, 1629.

Peirse, Sir H. B., 'Forest policy and legislation affecting Scotland, 1854–1953', *Scottish Forestry*, 8, 1954.

Pevsner, N., *Essex*, 1954.

Herefordshire, 1963.

Piggot, S., *Neolithic Cultures of the British Isles*, 1954.

Pliny, C. (trans. Holland, P.), *Natural Historie*, 1601.

(trans. H. Rackham, W. H. S. Jones, D. E. Eicholz), *Natural History*, 1938.

Powell, T. G. E., *The Celts*, 1958.

Price, Sir U., *An essay on the Picturesque*, 1796.

Essays on the Picturesque, 1798.

Qvist, A., *Epping Forest*, 1958.

Raistrick, A., *Quakers in Science and Industry*, 1950.

Dynasty of Ironfounders, 1953.

Ray, J., *Catalogus plantarum Angliae*, 1670.

Rehder, A., *Manual of cultivated trees and shrubs*, 1947.

Rennell, Lord, *Valley on the March: A history of . . . manors on the Herefordshire March of Wales*, 1958.

Reports of the Commissioners . . . into the state and condition of the woods, forests, and land revenues of the Crown, 1787–93.

Repton, H., *Observation on the theory and practice of landscape gardening*, 1803.

  An enquiry into the changes of taste in landscape gardening, 1806.

  and J. A., *Fragments on landscape gardening*, 1816.

Repton, H. (ed. Loudon, J. C.), *Landscape architecture of the late Humphry Repton, Esq.*, 1840.

Riat, G., *L'art des jardins*, 1899.

Ridley, H. N., *The Dispersal of Plants Throughout the World*, 1930.

Roper, L., *The Gardens in the Royal Park at Windsor*, 1959.

Rose, W., *The Village Carpenter*, 1937.

Rousseau, J. J., *Julia: or, the new Eloisa*, 1794.

Rowse, A. L., *The England of Elizabeth*, 1950.

Sands, M., *The Gardens of Hampton Court*, 1950.

Salzman, E. F., *Building in England Down to 1540*, 1952.

  English Trade in the Middle Ages, 1931.

Sargent, C. S., *Manual of the Trees of North America*, 1921.

Scott, Sir W., *Quarterly Review*, XXXVII, 1828.

Shaftesbury, Earl of, *Characteristicks*, 1773.

Shenstone, W., *The Works in Verse and Prose*, II, 1764.

Sieveking, A. F., *The Praise of Gardens*, 1899.

Siren, O., *China and the Gardens of Europe in the Eighteenth Century*, 1950.

Smith, J., *Historical Record of the Royal Botanic Gardens, Kew*, 1880.

Sorenson, J., *The Origin of Garden Art*, 1963.

Stebbing, E. P., *British Forestry*, 1916.

Steel, Sir S. S., 'History and activities of the Royal Scottish Forestry Society', *Scottish Forestry*, 1954.

Steuart, Sir H., *The Planter's Guide*, 1843.

Steven, H. M. and Carlile, A., *The Native Pinewoods of Scotland*, 1959.

Straker, E., *Wealden Iron*, 1931.

Stroud, D., *Capability Brown*, 1950.

  English Landscape Gardening of the Eighteenth and Early Nineteenth Centuries, 1951.

  Humphry Repton, 1962.

Strutt, J., *Sylva Britannica*, 1825.

  Sylva Scotica, n.d.

  Deliciae sylvarum, 1828.

Sturt, G., *The Wheelwright's Shop*, 1923.

Sueur, A. D. C. le, *A Guide to Burnham Beeches*, 1955.

Summerson, J., *Architecture in Britain 1530 to 1830*, 1953.

Switzer, S., *An Introduction to a General System of Hydrostatics and Hydraulics*, 1729.

Ichnographia rustica, 1742.

Tansley, A. G., *The British Isles and their Vegetation*, 1939.

Oaks and Oakwoods, 1952.

Taylor, W. L., 'Forest of Dean', *Forestry*, VIII, 1934.

Temple, Sir W., *Works*, 1720.

Thorn, J. R., 'Forestry and multiple land use in Wales', *Quarterly Journal of Forestry*, LVI, 1962.

Thorpe, H., 'The lord and his landscape', *Birmingham Archaelogical Society Transactions*, 80, 1965.

Transactions of the Highland and Agricultural Society of Scotland, XI, 1837.

Trusler, J., *Elements of Modern Gardening*, 1784.

Turner, W., *Names of Herbes*, 1548.

Herball, 1568.

Turrill, W. B., *The Royal Botanic Gardens, Kew*, 1959.

Wallace, A. F., 'An historical enquiry into forestry on a Highland estate', *Scottish Forestry*, 19, 1965.

Walpole, H., Earl of Orford, *The works of*, 1798.

(ed. Toynbee, Mrs P.), *Letters, 1903–25*.

Weston, R., *Tracts on Practical Agriculture and gardening*, 1773.

Whately, T., *Observations on Modern Gardening*, 1771.

Wheler, G., *A Journey into Greece*, 1782.

Whistler, L., *Sir John Vanbrugh*, 1938.

The Imagination of Vanbrugh and his Fellow Artists, 1954.

Wilcox, H. A., *The Woodlands and Marshlands of England*, 1933.

Williams, M., *William Shenstone*, 1935.

Woodward, M., 'Britain's black blot', *Pearson's Magazine*, 1905.

Worlidge, J., *Systemae agriculturae*, 1675.

Yapp, W. B., *Birds and Woods*, 1962.

Proceedings Botanical Society of the British Isles, 4, 1962.

Young, A., *Travels during the years 1787, 1788 and 1789*, 1794.

Zeuner, F. E., *Dating the Past*, 1946.

Index

Acacia, False, 156
Acer campestre (see Maple, Hedgerow)
  pseudoplatanus (see Sycamore)
Ackers, C. P., 178
Acorns, 19–21
Addison, Joseph, 93, 95, 145
Aesculus hippocastanum (see Chestnut,
  Horse)
Age, bronze, 15
  ice, 11
  iron, 15
  mesolithic, 12
  neolithic, 13–14
  paleolithic, 12
Agriculture, early, 14
Aislabie, J., 95
Albani, F., 99
Alder, 13, 49–50, Pl. 18
Aliens, naturalized, 14
Alnus glutinosa (see Alder)
Altdorfer, A., 98
America, United States of, English gardens
  in, 151–154
Anglo-Saxons, 62–66
Apple, Crab, 13, 57
Apples, Cultivated, 57
Araucaria araucana (see Monkey-puzzle)
Arnold Arboretum, 176
Ash, Mountain (see Rowan)
Ash and ashwoods, 48–49, Pls 16, 17
Aspen, 13, 53–54, Pl. 21
Audley End, Pl. 39
Austen, Jane, 128
Avenues, 35, 89–90, 174

Bagatelle, 146
Baker, Henry, 111
Bark, Oak, 25–26
Barocci, F., 98
Barry, Sir Charles, 174
Bean, W. J., *Trees and Shrubs Hardy in the
  British Isles*, 177
Beech and beechwoods, 36–40, Pl. 12
Benmore, 177, Pl. 55
Betula (see Birch)
  nana (see Birch, Dwarf)
  pubescens (see Birch)
  verrucosa (see Birch)
Birch, 12–15, 28–30, Pl. 7
  Dwarf, 12
Birds, 20, 25
Blackwood's Magazine, 140–141
Blaikie, T., 146
Bodnant, 177, Pl. 53
Bolotov, A., 146
Booth, J., 149
Borde Hill, 177
Bows, 34, 46
Box, 13
Bramblings, 38
Bridge, Land, 12
Bridgeman, Charles, 99
Brown, Lancelot ('Capability'), 104–107,
  139–140, Pls 33, 35, 39
Browning, Elizabeth Barrett, 132
Building, medieval, 72
Burke, Edmund, 97, 131
Burleigh, Lord, 80
Busch, J., 147
Buxus sempervirens (see Box)

Caerhays, 177
Campana, Roman, 94–95
Cannon, founding of, 79
Capercailzie, 43
Carpinus betulus (see Hornbeam)
Carvings, church, 22–23
Caserta, 150
Castanea sativa (see Chestnut, Spanish)
Castle Howard, 95, Pl. 29
Catherine II, of Russia, 146–147
Cattle, 128
Cedar, Atlas, 171
  Lebanon, 92, Pl. 32
  Western Red, or Thuja, 169, Pl. 46
Cedrus atlantica (see Cedar, Atlas)
  deodara (see Deodar)
  libani (see Cedar, Lebanon)
Celts, 60
Chamaecyparis lawsoniana (see Cypress, Lawson's)
  nootkatensis (see Cypress, Nootka)
  obtusa (see Hinoki)
  pisifera (see Cypress, Sawara)
Chambers, Sir William, 106–107
Charles I, 81
Charles II, 82–83
Charters, Trees in Anglo-Saxon, 65–66
Chase, medieval, 70, Pl. 23
Chatsworth, 173
Cherry, Bird, 13, 57
  Sweet, 13, 56–57
Chestnut, Horse, 86–88
  Spanish or Sweet, 13, 72–74, Pl. 24
China, western, 175–176
Cistercians, 20–21, Pl. 3
Claremont, 106
Clarens, 144–145
Claude, 96–99
Climate, atlantic, 13
  boreal, 12
  sub-arctic, 12
Clumber Park, 174, Pl. 48
Coal, 109
Cobbett, William, 156
Cobham, Lord, 95
Coffins, 26, 34
Coke, 109

Commissioners, Reports of, 112–117
Commonwealth, 82
Conkers, 87–88
Cook, M., 16
Coppice, chestnut, 73
Corriehalloch, Gorge of, Pl. 61
Corylus avellana (see Hazel)
Cowper, William, 128
Cox, E. H. M., 148
Crarae, 177
Crataegus (see Hawthorn)
  monogyna (see Hawthorn)
  oxyacanthoides (see Hawthorn)
Croome, 106
Cross-bill, 43
Crystal Palace, 172–173
Cupressus macrocarpa (see Cypress, Monterey)
Cypress, Lawson's, 169–170
  Monterey, 164
  Nootka, 159
  Sawara, 172
Czartoryska, Princess, 149

Darby, A., 109
D'Argenville, A. J. D., 99
David, J. P. A., 175
Davidia involucrata (see Tree, Handkerchief)
Dean, Forest of, 81, 84, 178
Defoe, Daniel, 99, 111
Delavay, J. M., 175
Delille, Abbé, 145
Deodar, 171
Domesday survey, 19, 38, 67–68
Donegall, Lord, 107
Douglas, David, 159, 161–165
Downing, A. J., 151–153
Downton Castle, 129
Dropmore, 162, Pls 45, 50
Dryas octopetala, 12
Dürer, A., tree painting by, 98

Eastnor, 171
Eastwoodhill, New Zealand, 177, Pl. 57
Ebbw Vale, Pl. 58
Edward VI, 80
Elder, 57–58

INDEX

Elizabeth I, 80
Elm, Cornish, 36
  Dutch, 33
  Hedgerow or English, 34–35, Pls 10, 11
  Huntingdon, 33
  Jersey, 36
  Smooth-leaved, 34–35
  Wych, 12–13, 33–34, Pl. 9
Elms, boundary, 34–35
Elwes, H. J., and Henry, A., *The Trees of Great Britain and Ireland*, 177
English Arboricultural Society, 158
Ermenonville, 104
Erody, Count, 149
Esterhazy, Count, 149
Eustace, Rev. J., 150
Evelyn, John, 82–84

Fagus sylvatica (see Beech)
Farges, P. G., 175
Ferme ornée, 100
Ficus sycomorus, 77
Fir, Douglas, 159, 163, Pl. 41
  Grandis, 164–165
  Nobilis, 165
Fisherwick, 107–108
Fodder, 34
Folk-lore, 31–32, 48–50, 51, 57–58, 123
Forestry, Board of Agriculture Committee on, 178
Forestry Commission, 180
Forests, royal and forest law, 67–70
  submerged, 59–60
  today's, 182–183
Forrest, G., 176
Foxley, 132
France, English gardens in, 142–146
Furnace, blast, 79

Gardening, Chinese, 95
  Cornish, 176
  Italian, 93
  Landscape, economics of, 107–108
  west of Scotland, 176
Garrick, David, 18
Gean (see Cherry, Sweet)
Germany, English gardens in, 149

Gilpin, Rev. William, 134
Gilpin, W. S., 137–139
Girardin, Marquis de, 104
Glenbervie, Lord, 155
Glendurgan, Pl. 49
Goats, 14, 63
Godwin, Dr H., 12
Goldcrest, 43
Goldfinch, 58
Gould, W., 148
Gwydyr Forest, Pl. 62

Ha-ha, 99
Hamilton, Hon. Charles, 101
Hammersmith, 150
Hartweg, C., 164
Hawthorn, 13, 30–32
Hazel, 12–13
Hedges, 35
Henry VIII, 70–80
Henry, A., 175–176
Hergest Croft, 177, Pl. 54
Hidcote, 177
Highland and Agricultural Society of Scotland, 157–158
Hinoki, 172
Hirschfield, C. C., 147
Holly, 13, 55–56
Hop-growing, 73
Hornbeam, 54
Horticultural Society of London, 159, 164
Hutchinson, W., 98–99

Ilex aquifolium (see Holly)
Ireland, 15
  Northern and Republic of, 180
Iron industry, 79–82
Italy, English gardens in, 149–150

Jackdaws, 20
James I, 81
Jardin anglais, Le, 142–146
Jay, 20
Jeffrey, J., 160, 170
Jekyll, Gertrude, 174
Juglans regia (see Walnut)
Juniper, 13
Juniperus communis (see Juniper)

Kames, Lord, 97
Kent, William, 99–101
Kielder, Pl. 60
Kingdon-Ward, F., 176
Knight, Richard Payne, 129–130

Lambert, A. B., 161, 164, 166
Lambert, G., 98
Larch, Dunkeld, 172
    European, 85, 117–119, Pl. 28
    Japanese, 172
Larix, eurolepis (see Larch, Dunkeld)
    europaea (see Larch, European)
    leptolepis (see Larch, Japanese)
Leasowes, The, 102–104
Ligne, Prince de, 145
Lime, 13
    Common or Hybrid, 54, 88–90, Pls 29, 48
    Large and Small-leaved, 54–55, Pl. 22
Linden (see Lime)
Lisle, Lord (later Duke of Northumberland), 80
Liverpool, Prince's Park, 173
Lobb, W., 159, 160, 167–9
Loddiges, C., 148
London, George, 95
Loudon, J. C., 132, 139, 142, 156
L'vov, N., 146

Malus sylvestris (see Apple, Crab)
Maple, Hedgerow or Field, 13, 52
Marie Antoinette, Queen, 143
Maries, C., 176
Marks, boundary, 26
Marnock, R., 173
Mast, Beech, 80
Masts, importation of, 72
May and May Day, 31
Meader, J., 148
Menzies, A., 126, 159, 162–163, 166
Middleton, Sir Charles, 112
Midland Re-Afforestation Society, 178
Milner, E. and H. E., 173
Mompesson, Sir G., 81
Monasteries, 20–21
    suppression of, 80
Monceau, 146

Monkey-puzzle, 126, 159, Pl. 45
Monza, 151
Mountains, English authors on, 94
    Gesner on, 93
    Petrarch on, 93
Mulberry, Black, 61
Münchausen, Baron von, 147
Munstead Wood, 174
Mynne, J., 80

Nesfield, W. A., 174
New Forest, 16, Pl. 40
New York, Central Park, 173
New Zealand, 177, Pl. 57
Normans, invasion by, 64–66
Nymans, 177

Oak, Brown, 25
    Durmast (sessile), 16–17, Pl. 4
    English (pedunculate), 17, Pl. 5
    Evergreen, 88
    Red, 122–123
    Turkey, 122
Oaks, ancient, 26–27
    and oakwoods, 12–14, 15–28, Pls 1, 2, 6, 40
    consumption of, in late 18th century, 120–121
    Irish, 26
    silviculture of, in 18th century, 120
    timber of, 23–26
Oakwood, ecological communities, 27–28
Offa's Dyke, 17
Olmstead, F. L., 154, 173
Oregon Association, 160

Painshill, 101, 130
Pannage, 64, 67–68
Park, medieval, 70–71
Parks, forest, 181
Patton, George (Lord Glenalmond), 160
Paxton, Sir Joseph, 172–174
Peterhof, 148
Pheasants, 20
Picea abies (see Spruce, Norway)
    sitchensis (see Spruce, Sitka)
Picturesque, The, 129–134

Pignons, 61
Pigs, 19–20, 64, 67–68
Pine, Corsican, 126
  Lodge-pole, 170–171
  Monterey, 163–164, Pl. 42
  Scots and pinewoods, 12–15, 40–43, Pls 13, 14
  Stone, 40, 61–62
  Weymouth, 121–122
Pineta, 161–162
Pinus contorta (see Pine, Lodge-pole)
  nigra maritima (see Pine, Corsican)
  pinaster, 40
  pinea (see Pine, Stone)
  radiata (see Pine, Monterey)
  strobus (see Pine, Weymouth)
  sylvestris (see Pine, Scots)
Pipes, wooden, 26, 61
Pitt, J., 112
Place-names, Anglo-Saxon origins of, 64–65
Plane, London, 90–92, Pl. 31
  North American, 90
  Oriental, 91
Plantation, first recorded timber, 80
Plants, Lusitanian, 11
Platanus hybrida (see Plane, London)
  occidentalis (see Plane, North American)
  orientalis (see Plane, Oriental)
Poland, English gardens in, 149
Pollen analysis, 11–12
Pope, Alexander, 95
Poplar, Black, 13–53
  Black Italian, 125
  Lombardy, 124–125, Pl. 36
Populus italica (see Poplar, Lombardy)
  nigra (see Poplar, Black)
  serotina (see Poplar, Black Italian)
  tremula (see Aspen)
Potemkin, Prince, 148
Poussin, Nicholas, 96, 99
Price, Major, 134
Price, Sir Uvedale, 131–134, 136, 137, 139, 176
Prunus avium (see Cherry, Sweet)
  padus (see Cherry, Bird)
  subhirtella, 32

Pseudotsuga menziesii (see Fir, Douglas)
Pulhawa, 149

Quercus (see Oak)
  borealis (see Oak, Red)
  cerris (see Oak, Turkey)
  ilex (see Oak, Evergreen)
  petraea (see Oak, Durmast)
  robur (see Oak, English)
Quicken (see Rowan)

Rabbit, 181
Redwood, Californian or Giant, 159, 165–166, Pl. 43
Repton, Humphry, 127–128, 134, Pls 37, 38
Riat, Georges, 142–145
Richardson, J., 99
Richens, R. H., 34
Rivers, 71
Robinia pseudacacia (see Acacia, False)
Robinson, William, 145, 172–173
Rock, J. F., 176
Romans, 60–62
Rooks, 20
Rosa, Salvator, 96, 99
Rousham, 99
Rousseau, J. J., 144–145
Rowallane, 177, Pl. 56
Rowan, 13, 50–52
  Chinese, 51
Royal Society of Arts, 111–112
Rubens, Peter Paul, 98
Rudding Park, Pl. 38
Russia, English gardens in, 146–149

Salix (see Willow)
  alba (see Willow, White)
  alba '*Tristis*' (see Willow, Weeping)
  babylonica (see Willow, Weeping)
  fragilis (see Willow, Crack)
Salvator's tree (see Chestnut, Spanish or Sweet)
Sambucus nigra (see Elder)
Sargent, C. S., 176
Savernake Forest, 69
Savill Gardens, 177

Schlich, Sir William, 178
Sckell, C., 135
Scott, Sir Walter, 132, 136
Scottish Arboricultural Society, 158
Sequoia sempervirens (see Redwood, Californian)
Sequoiadendron giganteum (see Wellingtonia)
Service, Wild, 52
Shaftesbury, Lord, 96
Sharawadgi, 95
Sheep, 14, 21
Sheffield Park, 177
Shenstone, William, 102–104
Silva, Count E., 150
Siskin, 43
Smith, George, 99
Sorbus aria (see Whitebeam)
  aucuparia (see Rowan)
  torminalis (see Service, Wild)
Soulie, J. A., 175
Southcote, P., 100–101
Spears, yew, 46
Spruce, Brewer's, Pl. 52
  Norway, 88, Pl. 30
  Sitka, 159, 162–163
Squirrel, grey, 181
Starlings, 20
Steuart, Sir Henry, 132, 136, 139–140
Stowe, 95
Strawberry-tree, 11, 13
Stroud, Dorothy, 105
Studley Royal, 95, Pl. 34
Sturt, George, 157
Swine (see Pigs)
Switzer, Stephen, 95, 97
Sycamore, 13, 76–78, Pl. 26

Tanning, 25–26
Tatton Park, Pl. 37
Taxus baccata (see Yew)
Thirlmere, 179
Thomson, James, 144
Thorn, Pl. 8
Thorn, place names including, 32
Thuja plicata (see Cedar, Western Red)
Tibet, 175–176

Tilia (see Lime)
  cordata (see Lime, Small-leaved)
  europaea (see Lime, Common)
  platyphyllos (see Lime, Broad-leaved)
Timber, imports of, 72, 156
  shortages of, 80, 109, 179
  transport of, 7
Tit, Crested, 43
Tollymore, Pl. 63
Topiary, 46
Townson, R., 149
Tree, Handkerchief, 176
Tsarskoe Selo, 147

Ulmus (see Elm)
  carpinifolia (see Elm, Smooth-leaved)
  cornubiensis (see Elm, Cornish)
  glabra (see Elm, Wych)
  procera (see Elm, Hedgerow)
  sarniensis (see Elm, Jersey)

Vanbrugh, Sir John, 97, 133
Vancouver, Capt. George, 159
Vaux, Calvert, 153, 154
Veitch, family of, 159–160, 171–172, 176
Verjuice, 57
Vesuvius, Mt., 93
Voght, Baron C. von, 149
Vyrnwy, Lake, 88, 182, Pl. 59

Wakehurst, 177
Walnut, 61, 74–76, Pl. 25
Walpole, Horace, 99–100
War, 1914–18, 180
  1939–45, 181
Warren, free, 71
Wars, Napoleonic, 17
Warwick Castle, 105
Weald, The, 81
Wellingtonia, 166–168, Pl. 44
Westonbirt, 137, 177, Pl. 52
Whigs, 96
White, T., 140
Whitebeam, 13, 51
Whitethorn (see Hawthorn)
Willow, 12
  Crack, 53, Pl. 20

Willow—*continued*
  Cricket-bat, 53
  Weeping, 123–124
  White, 52, Pl. 19
Wilson, E. H., 176
Wilson, G. F., 174, 176
Winchilsea, Countess of, 97
Wintour, Sir John, 81, Pl. 27
Wisley, 174–176
Wistman's Wood, 20

Witchen (see Rowan)
Wooburn Farm, 100–101
Wood, present-day uses of, 181–182
Wood-pigeons, 20
Wood-spirits, 22
Woodland, medieval, 70

Yeavering, palace at, 63
Yew, 13, 43–48, 126, Pl. 15
Young, Arthur, 143